West and Southwest
Wind Atlas

West and Southwest Wind Atlas

Dean DeHarpporte

State by State Maps
of Wind Speed and Wind Energy

Hawaii	Colorado
California	Arizona
Nevada	Kansas
Utah	Oklahoma
New Mexico	Texas

VNR VAN NOSTRAND REINHOLD COMPANY
NEW YORK CINCINNATI TORONTO LONDON MELBOURNE

Library of Congress Catalog Card Number: 83-675000
ISBN: 0-442-21823-0

Manufactured in the United States of America

Published by Van Nostrand Reinhold Company Inc.
135 West 50th Street
New York, New York 10020

Van Nostrand Reinhold Company Limited
Molly Millars Lane
Wokingham, Berkshire RG11 2PY, England

Van Nostrand Reinhold
480 Latrobe Street
Melbourne, Victoria 3000, Australia

Macmillan of Canada
Division of Gage Publishing Limited
164 Commander Boulevard
Agincourt, Ontario M1S 3C7, Canada

15 14 13 12 11 10 9 8 7 6 5 4 3 2 1

Library of Congress Cataloging in Publication Data

DeHarpporte, Dean.
    West and Southwest wind atlas.

    Includes index.
    1. Wind-power—Southwest, New—Maps.   2. Wind-power—
Hawaii—Maps.   3. Winds speed—Hawaii—Maps.
4. Winds speed—Southwest, New—Maps.   I. Title.
G1496.C84D3   1983   912′.155185′0979   83-675000
ISBN 0-442-21823-0

Preface

The *West and Southwest Wind Atlas* is based on research done for the U.S. Department of Energy by Battelle-Pacific Northwest Laboratory in 1980–81. All maps were reproduced directly from the following publications:

1. Wind Energy Resource Atlas: Volume 2—Hawaii and Pacific Islands Region, PNL-3995 WERA-11 UC-60, prepared for the U.S. Department of Energy by the University of Hawaii under agreement B-87918-A-L.
2. Wind Energy Resource Atlas: Volume 9—The Southwest Region, PNL-3195 WERA-9, prepared by Global Weather Consultants, Inc., for Pacific Northwest Laboratory under agreement B-87920-A-L.
3. Wind Energy Resource Atlas: Volume 8—The Southern Rocky Mountain Region, PNL-3195 WERA-8, prepared by ERT/Western Scientific Services, Inc., for Pacific Northwest Laboratory under agreement B-87921-A-L.
4. Wind Energy Resource Atlas: Volume 7—The South Central Region, PNL-3195 WERA-7 UC-60, prepared by Institute for Storm Research for Pacific Northwest Laboratory under agreement B-87923-A-L.

The Pacific Northwest Laboratory Atlases have been simplified and interpreted by Dean DeHarpporte, who is a professional meteorologist and a consultant in wind energy research.

Contents

1
Introduction

This Wind Speed Atlas contains detailed maps of average wind speed for Hawaii, California, Nevada, Utah, Colorado, Arizona, New Mexico, Kansas, Oklahoma, and Texas. To determine the average wind speed in your area, simply find your location on your state map. Other maps and graphs for your state show how wind speed varies through the cycle of the seasons and between day and night.

HOW TO USE THIS ATLAS

If the wind speed (averaged over the whole year) is less than 10 mph at your location, a wind machine will probably produce very little power and may never pay for itself. If your average wind speed is near or above 12 mph, however, you are located in a region where winds blow at a speed that most wind machines are designed for. In this location, a wind machine will provide adequate power and may pay for itself within a number of years. Areas where the average wind speed is above 15 mph are rare, but in those areas (some ridgetops, shore areas, and islands) electricity produced by wind power will be among the cheapest methods of producing power.

This Atlas describes average wind speed in terms of wind speed classes: the lowest, Class 1, has the lowest wind speeds, and the highest, Class 7, has the highest. In most areas of each state shown on the maps to be Class 1, the average wind speed is less than 10 mph. Most Class 7 areas, on the other hand, have average wind speeds of more than 16 mph. Between Class 1 and Class 7, the average wind speed is between about 10 and 16 mph, as shown in the following table:*

AVERAGE YEARLY WIND SPEED (mph)	CORRESPONDING WIND SPEED CLASS
Below 9.8	1
9.8-11.5	2
11.6-12.5	3
12.6-13.4	4
13.5-14.3	5
14.4-15.7	6
Above 15.7	7

*The relationship between wind speed class and the ranges of wind speed shown in the table are only approximate. The average wind speed at a particular location within a particular wind speed class may be slightly higher or lower than indicated by the table. This is true because the wind speed classes are actually defined by average wind power. For an explanation of the relationship between wind speed and wind power, refer to page 3.

Areas where the wind speed class is 6 or 7 are obviously the best locations for wind machines. Areas designated Class 3, 4, or 5 are good potential wind machine sites, whereas Class 2 areas are marginal. Most Class 1 areas are not suitable for wind machines; however, some Class 1 areas that are best exposed to the wind (on hilltops, for example) may have adequate wind speeds for wind machine operation.

The higher above ground a wind machine is installed, the stronger the wind speed. Wind speed increases about 1 mph for each 35-ft increase in height. Wind speeds are always higher on high ground or hilltops than in areas sheltered from the free flow of the wind.

In many of the maps included in this Atlas, mountainous areas are shaded gray. In these shaded areas, the wind class shown applies only to the exposed parts of the mountains. The exposed parts are ridges or crests, peaks, and, in some cases, passes. The valleys between the mountains and the lower portions of the slopes usually have low average wind speeds, ordinarily unsuitable for wind machines. When considering the siting of a wind machine in a valley, keep in mind that if the valley is located on a portion of a map shaded gray, the wind speed class indicated does not apply to the lower portions of the valley. Rather, the wind speed class in the valley is not shown but is probably substantially lower than the wind speed class that applies to the surrounding mountain summits.

Although this Atlas contains the newest and most accurate information on wind speeds available, there are undoubtedly borderline or remote areas where the actual wind speed varies by one or more classes from the class shown here. The only way to be positive that wind speeds are high enough (or too low) for the use of a wind machine at your location is to measure the wind speed for at least three months, and preferably for a whole year.

VARIATION OF AVERAGE WIND SPEED BY SEASON

The variation of wind speed by season is an important consideration in choosing a wind machine. In Hawaii, wind speeds are usually strongest in summer. The most appropriate use for a wind machine in Hawaii might therefore be to provide electricity for air conditioning. In California–Nevada and the Southwest, wind speeds are usually strongest in the spring. A wind machine used for heating a house during the cool part of spring might therefore be an appropriate choice for these states. Of course, if a wind machine is to be used only for the generation of electricity that will be independent of the electric utility, the wind machine will need to be large enough to generate sufficient power during the season when speeds are lowest (this season being autumn in most parts of Hawaii and summer or autumn in California–Nevada and the Southwest).

An option would be to choose a wind machine sufficiently large to produce enough electricity for only part of the time during the season of lowest wind speed and to rely on utility power when winds are calm or an unusually large amount of electricity is needed. If this option is chosen, there may be more than enough electricity generated by the wind machine during the season when winds are strongest. In this case, electricity will flow away from the wind machine into the electric utility wires where it will be routed to other utility customers. The utility is obligated by federal law to pay the wind machine owner a fair price for this electricity.

If complete independence from the local electric utility is desired, wind-machine-generated electricity may be stored in batteries. When winds are low or calm, the stored electricity can then be used as needed. The disadvantage of this option is the loss of about 25 percent of the electricity in the process of storing it and the high cost of the many batteries needed to store sufficient electricity to tide you over periods of light winds.

Some wind machines are made to produce heat rather than electricity. These wind machines, of course, are designed to take advantage of the strong winds of winter that blow over mountain crests in California–Nevada and over the plains in the Southwest.

VARIATION OF AVERAGE WIND SPEED BY DAY AND NIGHT

The change of wind speed with the hour of the day may affect your choice of wind machine. Usually, wind speeds are strongest during early afternoon and weakest at night. A wind machine might therefore provide enough electricity to run appliances during the day but less than enough for lighting purposes at night. To accommodate the differences in the amount of electricity generated, wind machine owners may choose to use electricity from the local utility or electricity stored in batteries.

Winds in Hawaii, California–Nevada, and the Southwest are as much as 100 percent stronger during the afternoon than at dawn and most of the night. The greatest day–night variation occurs during spring and summer; the least, during winter. On mountain ridges, there is only a small variation of wind speed from night to day. In some elevated mountain areas, winds may even be stronger during the night than during the day.

RELATIONSHIP OF WIND SPEED AND WIND POWER

The force of wind on a wind machine blade is proportional to the density of the air and the cube of the wind speed. Measurement of the wind energy available to turn the machine is accomplished by multiplying the air density by the cube of the wind speed. *Half* the air density multiplied by the cube of the wind speed is called the *wind power*. Wind power is the true measure of the force on a blade and is a better indicator of the amount of energy a wind machine may generate than wind speed itself.

Wind power is measured in units of Watts per square meter. Unfamiliarity with this measurement should not be important because it is only necessary to compare wind power (as an alternative to comparing wind speed) between potential wind machine sites.

The wind speed classes used in this Atlas are actually defined by wind power values. The relationship between wind power and wind speed class is shown in the following table:

WIND SPEED CLASS	WIND POWER (WATTS PER SQ. METER)
1	Below 100
2	100–150
3	150–200
4	200–250
5	250–300
6	300–400
7	400–1000

WIND SPEED AND WIND POWER DATA

At the conclusion of Sections 2, 3, and 4, there are tables to indicate the average wind power and wind speed at various locations in Hawaii, California–Nevada, and the Southwest. Included are all locations in these regions where wind speeds have been reliably measured over a long enough period to provide meaningful data. In these tables, wind power and wind speed are estimated at a height of 33 feet above ground level—the standard height for wind measurements. The 33-ft estimates are based on measurements taken at various ground levels. Since wind speed increases by about 1 mph for each 35 feet of elevation above ground, the average wind speed at the preferred level of wind machine installation (60 to 100 ft) is approximately 1 to 2 mph greater than that shown in these tables.

ESTIMATING A WIND MACHINE'S REDUCTION OF ELECTRIC BILLS

This Atlas makes it possible for you to estimate the amount of money you can save on electric bills by operating a wind machine. You need to know only three things:

1. *The wind speed class for the area where the wind machine will be installed.* Find your location on your state map to determine the appropriate wind speed class. Use either the map that shows the annual average wind speed class or the map that applies to the season in which you are interested.
2. *The rating of the wind machine you are considering purchasing.* Wind machines are rated by the maximum amount of electricity (in kilowatts, or kW) that they can produce when the wind is blowing strongly. Wind machines rated at from 4 to

10 kW provide a substantial fraction of the electricity used by the average household. A 4-kW wind machine costs about $10,000 (installed); a 10-kW wind machine, about $25,000. Of course, prices may be higher or lower depending upon the manufacturer, the height of the tower supporting the machine, the difficulty of installation, and many other factors.

3. *The cost of electricity in your area.* To determine that cost, call your electric company or look at your bill, and divide the total bill by the number of kilowatt-hours used. The cost should be calculated in *cents* per kilowatt-hour (not dollars per kilowatt-hour).

Now, to calculate the amount that your wind machine will reduce your *monthly* electric bills, multiply as follows:

$$\begin{pmatrix} \text{Wind} \\ \text{Speed} \\ \text{Class} \end{pmatrix} \times \begin{pmatrix} \text{Wind Machine} \\ \text{Rating in} \\ \text{Kilowatts} \end{pmatrix} \times \begin{pmatrix} \text{Electricity Cost} \\ \text{in Cents per} \\ \text{Kilowatt Hour} \end{pmatrix} \times \begin{pmatrix} \text{Units} \\ \text{Factor*} \\ \text{of 0.5} \end{pmatrix} = \begin{pmatrix} \text{Dollars} \\ \text{Saved} \\ \text{Per Month} \end{pmatrix}$$

Example: 3 × 4 × 7 × 0.5 = $42.00

A wind machine rated at 4 kW was used in this example. A 10-kW machine would save approximately $105.00 per month.

This calculation is only an approximation of the actual amount of money you can save. For example, remember that the wind speed class shown by this Atlas is only an estimate of the actual wind speed at your location. Wind speeds should be measured for at least three months before you decide on the machine best suited to your needs. Other factors that may affect the amount of money you can save are the following:

1. *The wind machine should be connected to available electric power lines.* The calculation of money saved is valid only when the wind machine is installed in such a way that it can feed power into the utility lines when you don't require the power. Federal law requires utilities to buy your wind-produced electricity at a cost that is only slightly lower than what you must pay to buy conventional electricity from the utility. If your wind machine is in a remote area, or if you don't take the trouble to hook it up to utility lines, the wasted electricity can cost you 50 percent or more of your savings. Of course, if you have a very small wind machine (rated at less than 1 kW), no electricity (or money) will be wasted. The same holds true if your house or business is so large that it uses as much power as your wind machine can generate.

2. *Raising the wind machine higher above the ground will increase savings.* The calculation of savings is based on a wind-

*Units factor is always 0.5.

machine height of about 60 feet above ground level—the height recommended by many wind machine manufacturers. Since wind speed increases in accordance with height above ground, an increase in the height of your wind machine from 60 to 100 ft, for example, could increase savings by 30 percent.

Wind speed increases most rapidly with height over forested or hilly terrain. It is important to install your wind machine so that its blades completely clear the level of the tallest trees, even if those trees are hundreds of feet away. Placing your machine atop the highest hill in the area (or nearly the highest) can increase savings substantially beyond those calculated because an exposed hilltop may increase the wind speed dramatically. The increase of wind speed with height is least dramatic over flat, treeless ground and near oceans and large lakes. Even in these areas, however, considerable savings can be achieved by increasing the height of your tower.

Of course, a higher tower costs more. An increase in tower height from 60 to 100 ft usually costs several thousand dollars. Since this cost is readily recovered, however, by the increased savings resulting from the availability of higher winds, many manufacturers now recommend that their wind machines be installed at 80 to 100 feet above ground level.

3. *Purchasing an efficient wind machine will increase savings.* Before shopping for a wind machine, learn how the efficiency of wind machines is determined. You will find that some of them, although equal in size and rating to others, are more efficient in converting wind to electricity. Since wind machine technology is still developing, some brands of machines are not only inefficient, but poorly constructed. These brands break down repeatedly and never repay their cost through electricity savings.

Shop for a wind machine in terms of its efficiency and durability. Several well-constructed brands are available that will convert wind to electricity in such a highly efficient manner that they can mean years of electricity savings.

2
Hawaii

- Kauai and Niihau
- Oahu
- Maui, Molokai, Lanai, and Kahoolawe
- Hawaii

GENERAL INFORMATION

Almost every one of the Hawaiian Islands has regions of at least moderate wind speeds, and portions of several of the islands have exceptionally strong and steady winds. The steadiness of the winds is important because it makes the generation of energy from the power of the wind more reliable. The use of wind power looms large in Hawaii's determined effort to become energy self-sufficient well before the turn of the century. Toward this end, Hawaiian wind farms —clusterings of hundreds of large commercial-type wind machines—were being planned in the early 1980s to help replace electricity generated by burning oil.

Average wind speeds in Hawaii vary enormously from island to island, mountain to shore, open land to dense forest, and windward to leeward of the trade winds. The steady, reliable flow of air across the islands is provided by these tropical winds, now ebbing, now blowing more strongly, but rarely interrupted long enough for their return to be noticed.

Since the trade winds blow only in the lowest few thousand feet of the atmosphere, the higher slopes of the volcanoes do not experience winds as strong or as steady as the lower elevations of the islands. The most favorable winds for the production of energy are found on the open land that slopes upward from the island shores and on the elevated peninsulas jutting toward the ocean. Not all such land experiences favorable winds because mountains block or deflect the flow of the trade winds in some regions. Other portions of the islands that are especially windy are the upper slopes and summits of the lower mountain ranges (particularly on Oahu) and some of the broad mountain passes.

YEARLY AVERAGE WIND SPEEDS

Kauai and Niihau

Yearly average wind speeds for Kauai and Niihau are shown in Fig. 1. Kauai has winds as high as Class 6 (14.3 to 15.7 mph) on both its

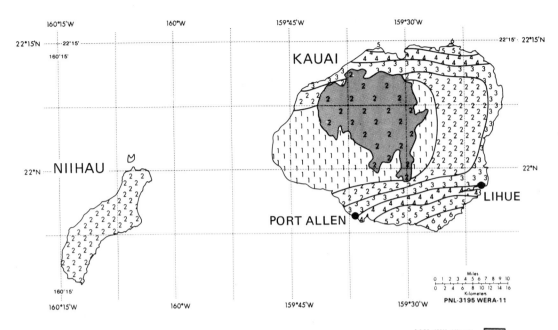

AVERAGE YEARLY WIND SPEED (MPH)	CORRESPONDING WIND SPEED CLASS
Below 9.8	1
9.8–11.5	2
11.6–12.5	3
12.6–13.4	4
13.5–14.3	5
14.4–15.7	6
Above 15.7	7

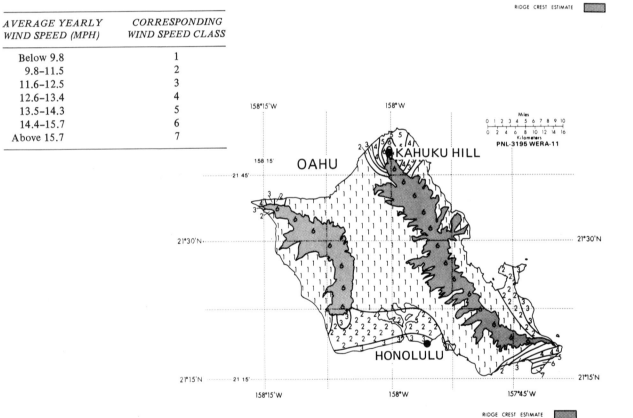

Fig. 1   Yearly average wind speeds in Niihau, Kauai, and Oahu.

northern and southeastern coasts. Average speeds decrease toward Mt. Waialeale (one of the rainiest places in the world), which occupies the center of the island. The more exposed crests of the central mountains (shaded portions of Fig. 1) have Class 2 winds. Winds in sheltered portions of the shaded area are probably only Class 1.

Wind speeds on Niihau generally average Class 2, but those on the tops of some of the higher hills may be somewhat stronger.

Oahu

Wind speeds averaged over the year for Oahu are also shown in Fig. 1. Oahu, which has over 80 percent of the population of Hawaii and consumes 90 percent of the electricity, is fortunate to have extensive regions with strong and steady winds. These include the Kahuku peninsula and Koko Head, where speeds average as high as Class 7 and exceed Class 4 over a broad area. The tip of Kaena Point also has Class 4 winds, and Class 3 speeds occur along the immediate south shore from Honolulu westward. Class 6 winds are found on the crests of the Koolau and Waianae mountain ranges. The ruggedness of these mountains, however, and the extremely gusty character of their winds make their crests far less desirable wind machine sites than the much more accessible peninsulas. Most of the interior of Oahu and even most of the coastal areas experience only Class 1 winds.

Maui, Molokai, Lanai, and Kahoolawe

Yearly average wind speeds for Molokai, Maui, Lanai, and Kahoolawe are shown in Fig. 2.

The strongest winds on Maui occur in the valley separating the Haleakala and West Maui volcanoes. Speeds are normally Class 4 in the valley but culminate in a small Class 6 area near Maalaea Bay. The rugged upper portions of the volcanoes experience only Class 2 and 3 winds. Class 4 winds are found on the northern tip of Maui; Class 3 winds, on the southeast tip.

About half of Molokai experiences average wind speeds of Class 4 or more. Speeds increase northward from the center of the island and reach Class 7 at Ilio Point at the northwest tip. Winds over the southeast coast are Class 4. The lightest winds on Molokai, Class 2, are found in the high eastern mountains that poke above the trade winds.

The northern third of Lanai averages Class 4 winds, whereas the remainder of the island falls in the Class 3 range.

Uninhabited Kahoolawe normally averages only Class 2 winds.

Hawaii

The yearly average wind speeds of the "Big Island," Hawaii, are also shown in Fig. 2. Although most of the island experiences only Class 1 winds, regions of strong winds are sufficiently extensive for wind machines to provide electricity for the entire island.

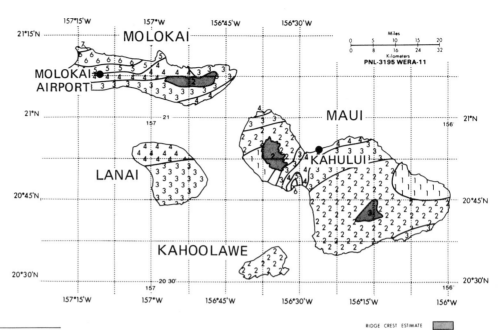

AVERAGE YEARLY WIND SPEED (MPH)	CORRESPONDING WIND SPEED CLASS
Below 9.8	1
9.8–11.5	2
11.6–12.5	3
12.6–13.4	4
13.5–14.3	5
14.4–15.7	6
Above 15.7	7

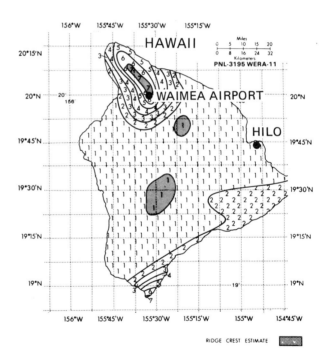

Fig. 2 Yearly average wind speeds in Molokai, Maui, Lanai, Kahoolawe, and Hawaii.

Two high volcanoes, Mauna Loa and Mauna Kea, block the trade winds, causing wind stagnation over most of the island. Diversion of the trade winds north of Mauna Kea, however, causes them to accelerate as they pass over the Waimea saddle and the Kohala Mountains. Rugged terrain on the northeast side of the Kohalas causes light wind speeds both on and between the mountains. But on the smooth uplands and mountain flanks and at Waimea, wind speeds exceed Class 4 over a wide area, sometimes reaching as high as Class 7.

A similar acceleration of winds over the south cape results in a smaller, but still significant, area of strong winds, again as high as Class 7 on the very tip of the cape. The remainder of the southeast coast experiences Class 2 winds.

SEASONAL AVERAGE WIND SPEEDS

Kauai and Niihau

On Kauai, the general pattern—light winds in the interior and in the mountains, with strongest winds on the southern and northern coasts—persists from season to season. On Niihau, there is no appreciable seasonal variability in average wind speed. Seasonal average wind speeds on Kauai and Niihau are shown for winter and spring in Fig. 3 and for summer and autumn in Fig. 4.

On Kauai, the pattern of light winds in the interior and strong winds on the south and north coasts persists through the year. Speeds on the north coast reach their highest value—Class 7—during summer. On the south coast, speeds average Class 6 during every season at Makahuena Point, but the stronger winds extend farthest west along the south coast and farthest inland during spring. Autumn is the season of lightest wind along both the south and north coasts.

Over Niihau, winds remain approximately Class 2 during all seasons.

The average monthly wind speeds at Lihue, Kauai (on the east coast) and Port Allen, Kauai (on the south coast) are shown in graphical form in Fig. 5. Neither is located in the region of highest wind speeds near Makahuena Point, but they are close enough to have favorable wind speeds. At both Lihue and Port Allen, the highest speeds occur during spring and summer and the lightest in autumn. The difference between the windiest and least windy seasons is about 3 to 4 mph.

Oahu

Seasonal wind speeds over the most populous of the islands, Oahu, are shown in Figs. 6 (winter and spring) and 7 (summer and autumn). Summer and spring are somewhat windier than the other two seasons over most of the island. Spring holds the edge over summer by about one wind speed class on the crests of the Koolau and Waianae Mountains, Kaneohe Point, and Kaena Point. But along the south shore, including the Pearl Harbor area and Waikiki Beach, speeds are Class 4 during summer and only Class 3 during spring. Over the windy shoul-

WINTER

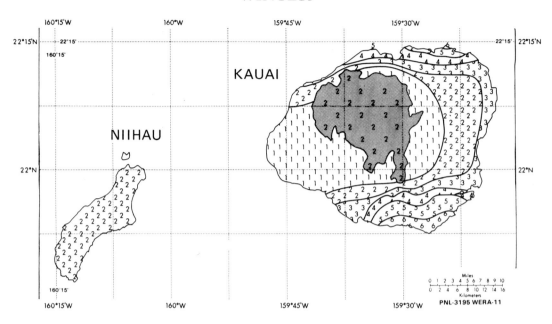

AVERAGE YEARLY WIND SPEED (MPH)	CORRESPONDING WIND SPEED CLASS
Below 9.8	1
9.8–11.5	2
11.6–12.5	3
12.6–13.4	4
13.5–14.3	5
14.4–15.7	6
Above 15.7	7

SPRING

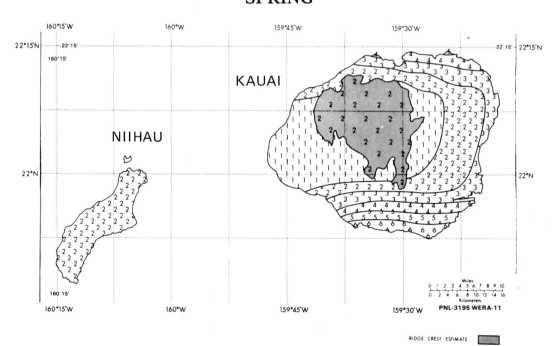

Fig. 3 Seasonal average wind speeds in Niihau and Kauai.

SUMMER

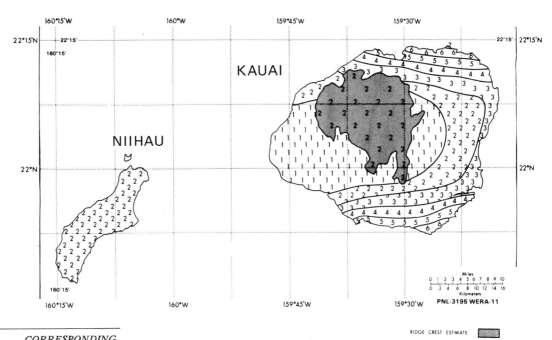

AVERAGE YEARLY WIND SPEED (MPH)	CORRESPONDING WIND SPEED CLASS
Below 9.8	1
9.8–11.5	2
11.6–12.5	3
12.6–13.4	4
13.5–14.3	5
14.4–15.7	6
Above 15.7	7

AUTUMN

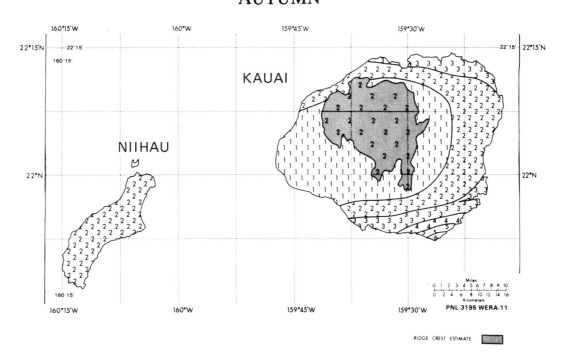

Fig. 4   Seasonal average wind speeds in Niihau and Kauai.

KAUAI AND OAHU

MONTHLY AVERAGE WIND SPEEDS

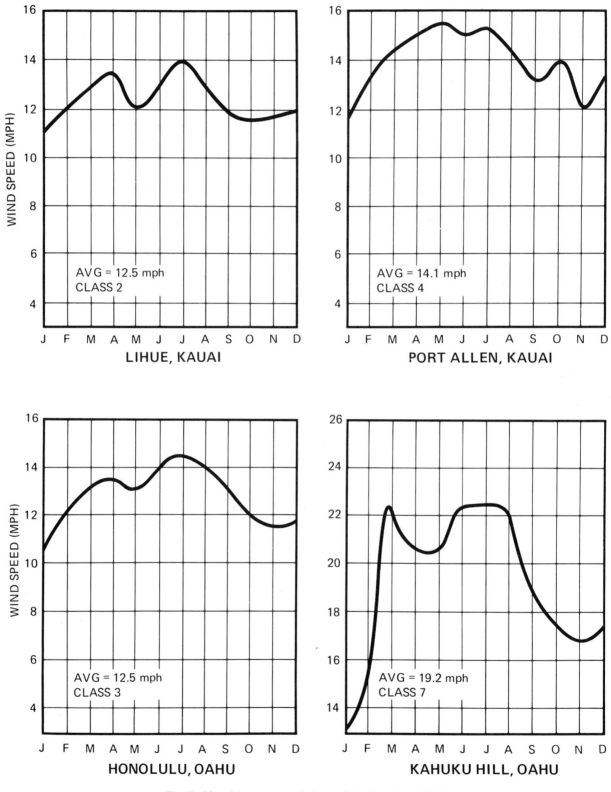

Fig. 5 Monthly average wind speeds in Kauai and Oahu.

der of Kahuku Hill, speeds are equally strong—Class 7—during both spring and summer and in autumn as well.

Average monthly speeds at Honolulu and at Kahuku Hill—a special University of Hawaii measurement station near the windiest point in the Kahuku Mountains—are shown in Fig. 5. The acceleration of the trade winds over this smooth hill causes wind speeds rivaling those in the Aleutian Islands. No matter which of the two is the windiest place in the United States, Kahuku's winds blow far more steadily than those in the Aleutians.

Kahuku wind speeds are strongest during March and again during late summer; winter speeds average some 9 mph lower. This pattern is typical of the elevated coastal regions of Oahu. At Honolulu, the same pattern is repeated but in a less pronounced fashion than in the windier parts of the island. Here, the difference between midsummer and midwinter speeds is only about 4 mph.

Maui, Molokai, Lanai, and Kahoolawe

Average seasonal wind speeds at this group of islands between Oahu and the Big Island are shown in Fig. 8 (winter and spring) and Fig. 9 (summer and autumn). Over most of these islands, the windiest seasons are also spring and summer, with winter not too far behind. The exception is the upper slopes and summit of Mt. Haleakala on Maui, where winter is windiest. Autumn is clearly the least windy season over all the islands. Over Lanai, winds are approximately one wind speed class lower during autumn than during the other three seasons; over Kahoolawe, about two classes lower. On Maui, nevertheless, a pocket of Class 6 winds persists, even in autumn, near Maalaea Bay.

Graphs showing the monthly average wind speeds at Molokai Airport (in the western interior of the island) and Kahului, Maui (on the north coast in the windy corridor between Maui's two volcanoes) are given in Fig. 10. At Molokai Airport, where the pattern is quite typical of the monthly variation over much of Molokai, wind speeds average 4 to 5 mph more during summer than the remainder of the year. The Kahului graph, too, reveals a speed maximum in summer, a lesser maximum during spring, and lower speeds during autumn and winter.

Hawaii

Over Hawaii, the general seasonal pattern of strongest winds in summer and lightest in autumn continues. Average speeds are shown in Fig. 11 for winter and spring and in Fig. 12 for summer and autumn. Although the crests of the Kohala mountains have Class 7 speeds during all seasons, even in that northern region the strongest winds affect less territory in other seasons, particularly autumn, than they do during summer. For example, at sea level at Upolu Point (the northernmost part of the Big Island), wind speeds average Class 5 in summer, Class 4 in spring, Class 3 in winter, and only Class 2 in autumn. Over the other region of strong winds—the South Cape—the extent of the

WINTER

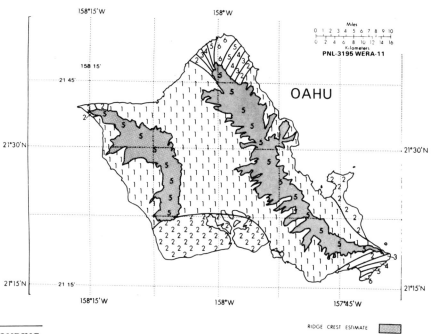

AVERAGE YEARLY WIND SPEED (MPH)	CORRESPONDING WIND SPEED CLASS
Below 9.8	1
9.8–11.5	2
11.6–12.5	3
12.6–13.4	4
13.5–14.3	5
14.4–15.7	6
Above 15.7	7

SPRING

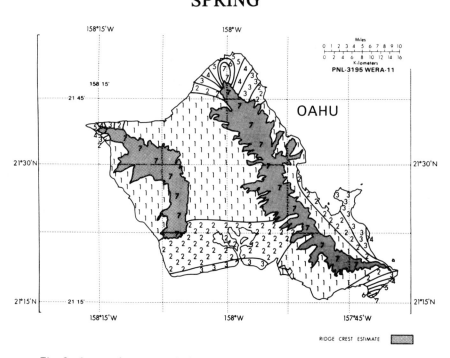

Fig. 6 Seasonal average wind speeds in Oahu.

SUMMER

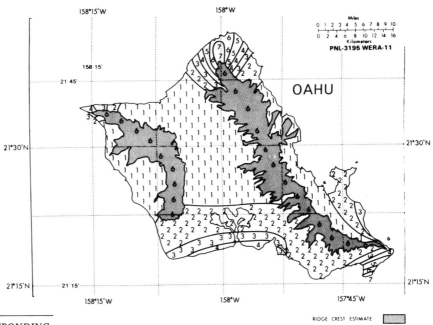

AVERAGE YEARLY WIND SPEED (MPH)	CORRESPONDING WIND SPEED CLASS
Below 9.8	1
9.8–11.5	2
11.6–12.5	3
12.6–13.4	4
13.5–14.3	5
14.4–15.7	6
Above 15.7	7

AUTUMN

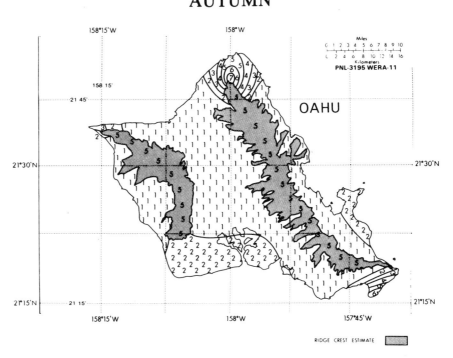

Fig. 7 Seasonal average wind speeds in Oahu.

WINTER

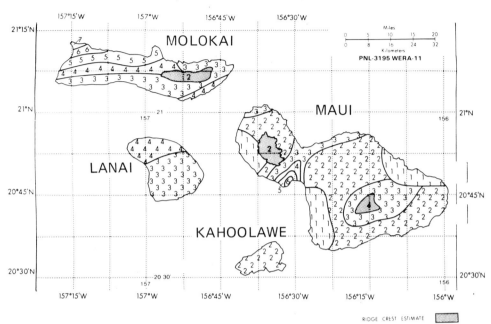

AVERAGE YEARLY WIND SPEED (MPH)	CORRESPONDING WIND SPEED CLASS
Below 9.8	1
9.8–11.5	2
11.6–12.5	3
12.6–13.4	4
13.5–14.3	5
14.4–15.7	6
Above 15.7	7

SPRING

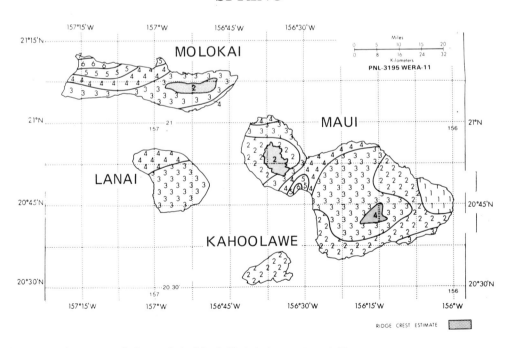

Fig. 8   Seasonal average wind speeds in Maui, Molokai, Lanai, and Kahoolawe.

SUMMER

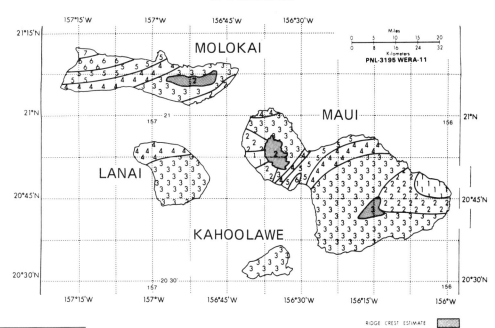

AVERAGE YEARLY WIND SPEED (MPH)	CORRESPONDING WIND SPEED CLASS
Below 9.8	1
9.8–11.5	2
11.6–12.5	3
12.6–13.4	4
13.5–14.3	5
14.4–15.7	6
Above 15.7	7

AUTUMN

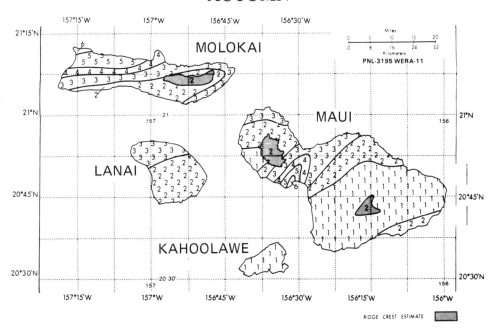

Fig. 9 Seasonal average wind speeds in Maui, Molokai, Lanai, and Kahoolawe.

MOLOKAI, MAUI, AND HAWAII

MONTHLY AVERAGE WIND SPEEDS

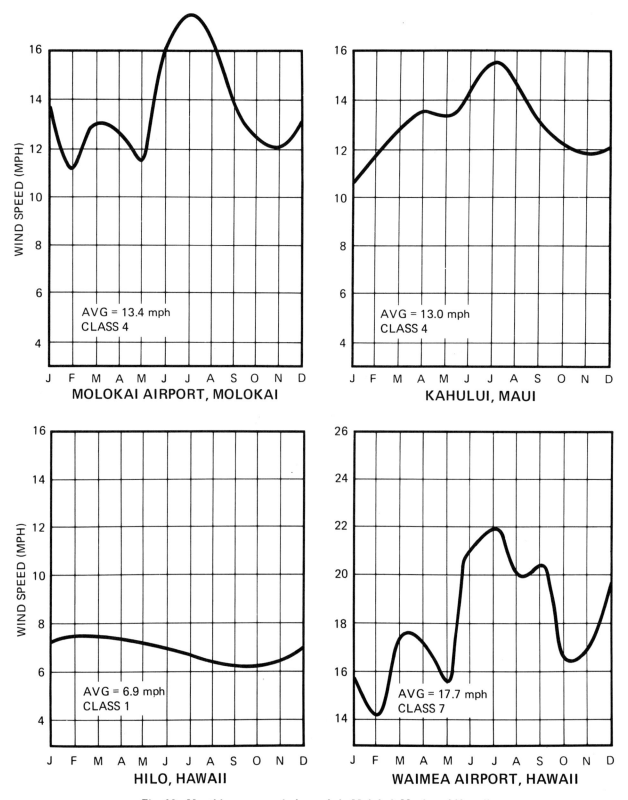

Fig. 10   Monthly average wind speeds in Molokai, Maui, and Hawaii.

stronger winds during autumn is also restricted compared to what it is in other seasons.

On the upper slopes and summits of the two volcanoes, Mauna Kea and Mauna Loa, speeds average Class 2 in winter and Class 1 during other seasons. The speeds are stronger during winter because these high elevations lie above the trade winds.

Monthly average wind speeds at Hilo (on the west coast) and at Waimea Airport (between Mauna Kea and the Kohala Mountains) are shown in Fig. 10. At Hilo, where the trade winds are deflected to the north and south by the massive volcanoes, wind speeds are typical of those in all of Hawaii's Class 1 regions—light throughout the year. At Waimea Airport, on the other hand, the trade winds are accelerated by the surrounding terrain, as they are over the Kohala Mountains and the South Cape. That the wind speed peak here should occur in midsummer is obvious. Speeds vary erratically from month to month during the remainder of the year but are lower than in summer by 2 to 8 mph.

AVERAGE WIND SPEEDS BY DAY AND NIGHT

In general, wind speeds are higher during the day than at night in Hawaii, especially well inland and at those coastal locations where the normal flow of the trade winds is interrupted by mountains. At higher elevations, this day–night wind speed pattern varies; in some cases, winds are stronger at night than during the day over mountain crests.

The day-to-night variability is greatest in summer and least in winter over most regions of low elevation in all of the Hawaiian Islands. At the higher elevations, other patterns may prevail.

Kauai, Niihau, and Oahu

The daily pattern of wind speed at Lihue and Port Allen on Kauai and at Honolulu and Kahuku Hill on Oahu is shown in Fig. 13. Lihue's location on the coast where the trade winds blow freely causes the day–night difference to be relatively small—2 mph. In stark contrast is the 7-mph difference at Port Allen, where the stronger winds result from the interaction of the trade winds with the terrain. At both locations, the highest speeds occur during early afternoon and the lowest near dawn.

At Honolulu, near sea level, the day–night difference is also about 7 mph, whereas the difference is only about 3 mph at the very windy Kahuku Hill location. Measurements on Oahu's Wainae and Koolau Mountains indicate that wind speeds are actually higher at night than during the day on the crests.

Molokai, Maui, Lanai, Kahoolawe, and Hawaii

Hourly average wind speeds for Molokai Airport on Molokai, for Kahului on Maui, and for Hilo and Waimea Airport on the Big Island are shown in Fig. 14. The same pattern—highest speeds during early afternoon and lowest speeds near sunrise—occurs at all four

WINTER

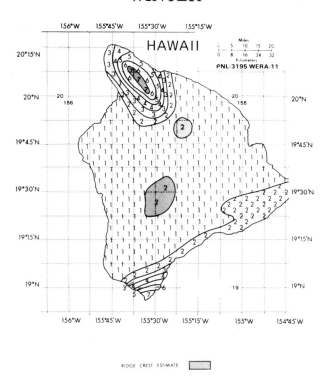

AVERAGE YEARLY WIND SPEED (MPH)	CORRESPONDING WIND SPEED CLASS
Below 9.8	1
9.8–11.5	2
11.6–12.5	3
12.6–13.4	4
13.5–14.3	5
14.4–15.7	6
Above 15.7	7

SPRING

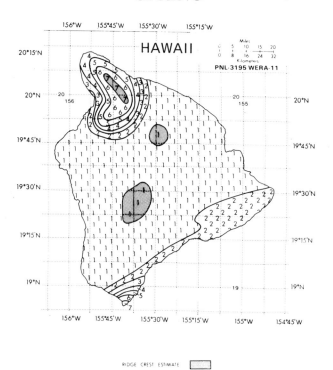

Fig. 11 Seasonal average wind speeds in Hawaii.

SUMMER

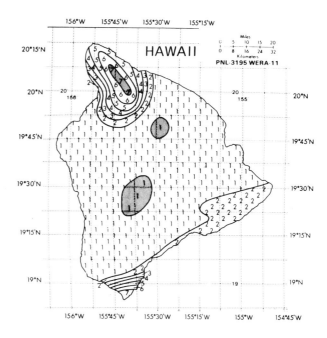

RIDGE CREST ESTIMATE

AVERAGE YEARLY WIND SPEED (MPH)	CORRESPONDING WIND SPEED CLASS
Below 9.8	1
9.8–11.5	2
11.6–12.5	3
12.6–13.4	4
13.5–14.3	5
14.4–15.7	6
Above 15.7	7

AUTUMN

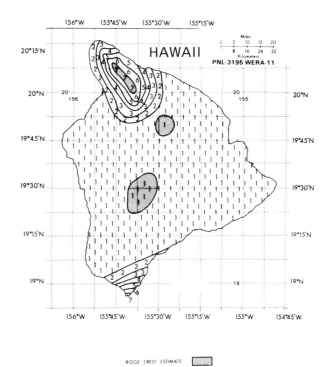

RIDGE CREST ESTIMATE

Fig. 12 Seasonal average wind speeds in Hawaii.

KAUAI AND OAHU

HOURLY AVERAGE WIND SPEEDS

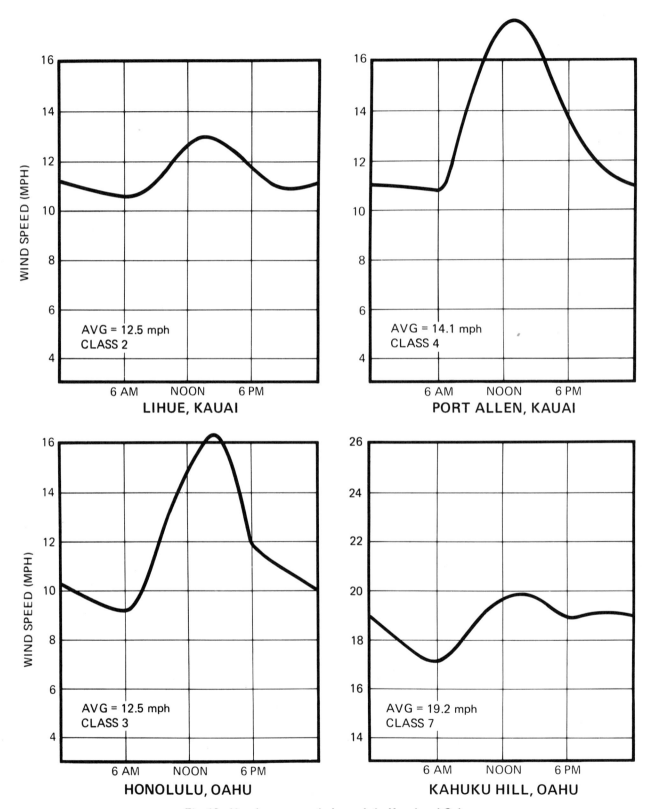

Fig. 13 Hourly average wind speeds in Kauai and Oahu.

MOLOKAI, MAUI, AND HAWAII

HOURLY AVERAGE WIND SPEEDS

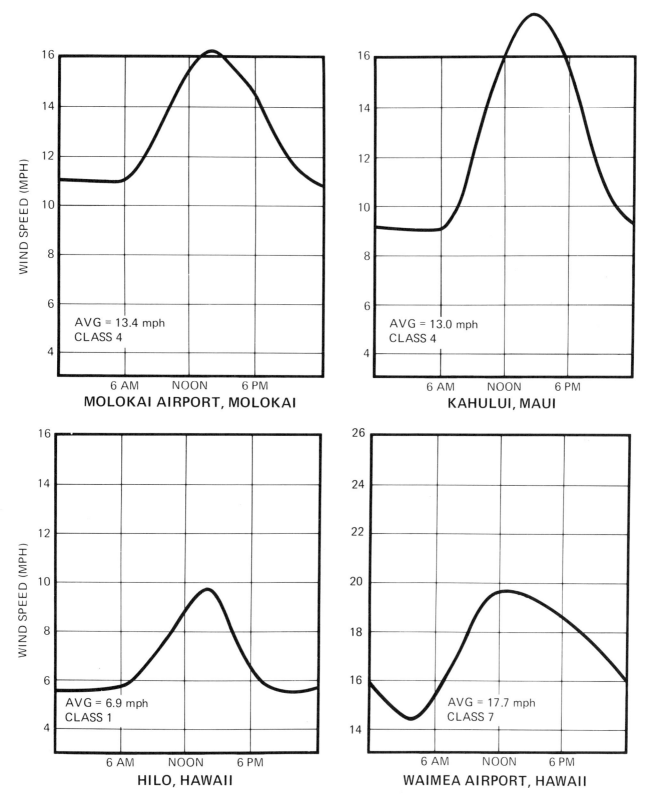

Fig. 14 Hourly average wind speeds in Molokai, Maui, and Hawaii.

locations, despite their diverse elevations and varying exposure to the trade winds. The difference between the highest and lowest wind speeds of the 24-hour cycle ranges from 9 mph at Kahului on Maui to only about 5 mph at the three other locations.

WIND SPEED AND WIND POWER AT VARIOUS LOCATIONS IN HAWAII

The table that follows shows the yearly average wind speed and the yearly average wind power at each location in Hawaii where winds are measured frequently and reliably. Not enough measurements have been made at other locations to provide the basis for computing reliable yearly averages. (For a definition of wind power and its relationship to average wind speed, refer to page 3.)

TOWN, CITY, OR PLACE	FACILITY	YEARLY AVERAGE WIND SPEED (MPH AT 33 FT ABOVE GROUND)	YEARLY AVERAGE WIND POWER (WATTS PER SQ. METER)
		KAUAI	
Barking Sands	Barking Sands Naval Facility	5.1	36
Lihue	Lihue Airport	12.5	148
Port Allen	Civil Aeronautics Administration (CAA)	14.1	224
		OAHU	
Barbers Point	Barbers Point Naval Air Facility	9.0	77
Honolulu	Honolulu Airport	12.5	167
Kaena Pt. Tower	University of Hawaii	13.2	233
Kahuku Hill	Lawrence Livermore Laboratory	19.2	563
Kaneohe Bay	Marine Corps Air Station	11.4	138
Koko Head	University of Hawaii	17.7	406
Tantalus Tower	University of Hawaii	16.6	472
Wahiawa	Wheeler Air Force Base	6.9	58
		MAUI	
Kahului	Kahului Airport	13.0	211
Puunene	Puunene CAA	10.1	121
		MOLOKAI	
Molokai	Molokai Airport	13.4	210
		HAWAII	
Hilo	Hilo Airport	6.9	33
Kahua Ranch	University of Hawaii	25.5	1569
Waimea Airport	University of Hawaii	17.7	515
		FRENCH FRIGATE SHOALS	
French Frigate Shoals	Naval Air Station	15.0	289

3
California – Nevada

- Northern California
- Southern California
- Nevada

GENERAL INFORMATION

California and Nevada contain, or are near, almost every conceivable element that influences wind speed: mountains (high, low, and oriented in every direction), valleys (from the very large to the very small), bays, peninsulas, rocky coastlines, islands, forests, and deserts. As a result, average wind speeds vary erratically from very strong (in a few widely scattered places) to moderate or very light (in most, but also scattered, places). The map of wind speed classes in the California–Nevada region appears in Fig. 15, and it is a complicated map, indeed. Details of average wind speeds are provided in separate sections for each of three areas—Northern California, Southern California, and Nevada.

Most of the strong winds occur on mountain tops, and the higher the mountains, the stronger the winds. It must be remembered, however, that the higher mountain summits of this region are usually inaccessible and that when winds are strongest, during winter, the high country is often under tons of snow and ice. More accessible regions of strong wind can be found along some exposed coastal points and in the gaps in the coastal mountain ranges. Some of these gaps are not only accessible but also very near large population centers, making them ideal sites for wind machines.

There are large differences in wind speed from season to season over many parts of California and Nevada. The seasons of strongest wind are shown in Fig. 16. As a rule, winter is the windiest season in most mountain regions, whereas spring is windiest in regions with level terrain. Exceptions are the summits of the western part of the Sierra Nevada Mountains and the crests of some of the other mountains, where spring is windier than winter. Along a portion of the California coast, the windiest season is summer.

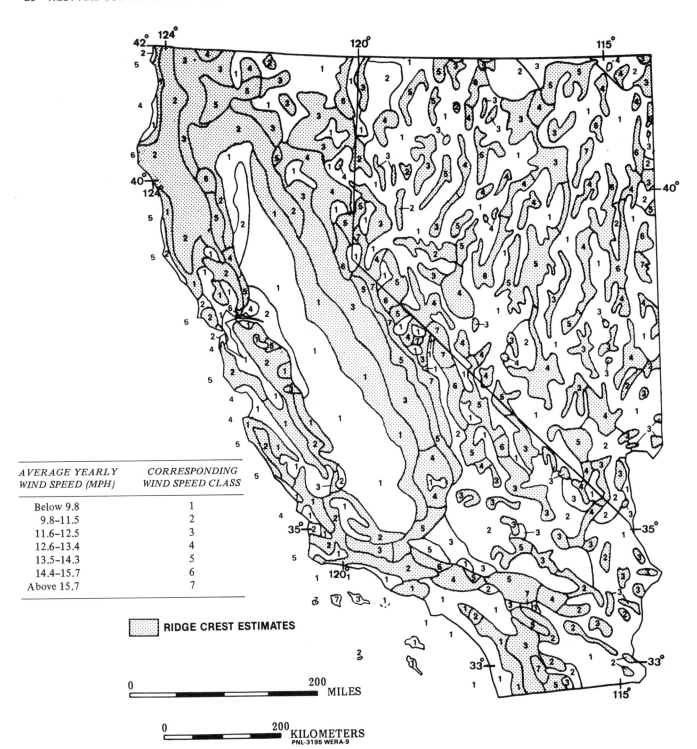

AVERAGE YEARLY WIND SPEED (MPH)	CORRESPONDING WIND SPEED CLASS
Below 9.8	1
9.8–11.5	2
11.6–12.5	3
12.6–13.4	4
13.5–14.3	5
14.4–15.7	6
Above 15.7	7

RIDGE CREST ESTIMATES

0   200
                                MILES

0   200
                                KILOMETERS
                            PNL-3195 WERA-9

Fig. 15   Yearly average wind speeds in California and Nevada.

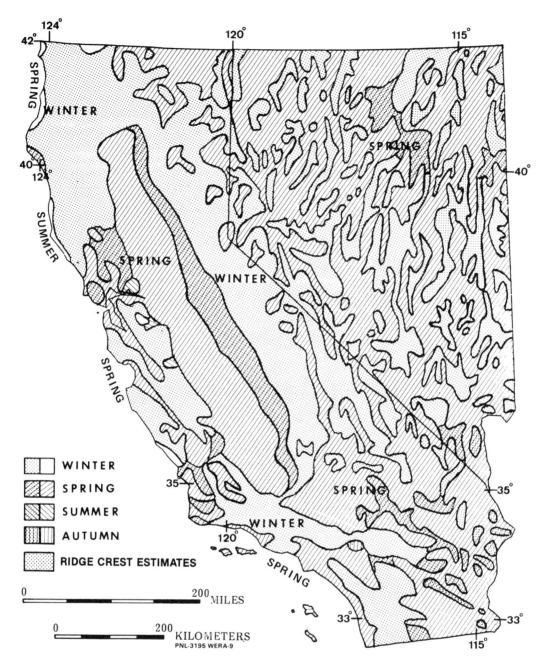

Fig. 16 Seasons of maximum wind speeds in California and Nevada.

NORTHERN CALIFORNIA

YEARLY AVERAGE WIND SPEEDS

Although wind speeds are high on the crests of the mountains of Northern California, these crests are usually hard to get to and are buffeted by severe winter weather. Most of the flatland areas have low average wind speeds, but some coastal points are windy enough to serve as favorable locations for wind machines. The best regions for the production of energy by wind power, however, are in two broad gaps in the coastal range—Pacheco Pass (about 40 miles southeast of San Jose) and Altamont Pass (on Interstate 580 east of Oakland)— and in the Carquinez Straights, where the Sacramento River meets San Francisco Bay.

Yearly average wind speeds in Northern California are shown in Fig. 17. The remote spine of the Sierra Nevada Mountains is blasted by Class 7 winds (more than 15.7 mph), and most mountain peaks and ridges higher than 7000 ft average Class 4 winds. The lower summits of the Coast Range have mostly Class 2 winds. Wind speeds average much lower on the lower mountain slopes and in the intervening valleys.

Within the Pacheco and Altamont Passes and on the shores of the Carquinez Straights, winds average from Class 4 to Class 6. Because of the proximity of these locations to the burgeoning San Francisco Bay population center, they have become recognized as valuable wind energy production sites. As a result, construction of "wind farms"— arrays of hundreds of wind machines covering many acres—began in Altamont Pass in the early 1980s.

Favorable Class 4 to Class 6 winds blow just offshore along the entire northern California coast. Along most of the coastline, these winds are broken up by the steep, rocky terrain. Yet, some points— particularly the parts of Cape Mendocino that extend westward into the ocean and are exposed to the strongest winds, which usually come from the north or south—experience yearly average wind speeds of Class 5 or Class 6.

Unfortunately, most of the more populated areas—including the broad Central Valley and the plateaus and valleys east of the Sierra Nevada Mountains—experience only Class 1 winds.

SEASONAL AVERAGE WIND SPEEDS

Average wind speeds vary considerably from season to season in Northern California, as Fig. 18, for winter and summer, and Fig. 19, for spring and autumn, show. Winter and spring are the windiest seasons, and summer and autumn the least windy.

Winter is the season when winds on the mountain crests are the strongest. Average speeds are Class 7 on many of the higher peaks of the Sierra Nevada Mountains as well as on peaks of that part of the Coast Range that protrudes into Northern California from Oregon. Even some of the higher peaks of the remainder of the Coast Range

AVERAGE YEARLY WIND SPEED (MPH)	CORRESPONDING WIND SPEED CLASS
Below 9.8	1
9.8–11.5	2
11.6–12.5	3
12.6–13.4	4
13.5–14.3	5
14.4–15.7	6
Above 15.7	7

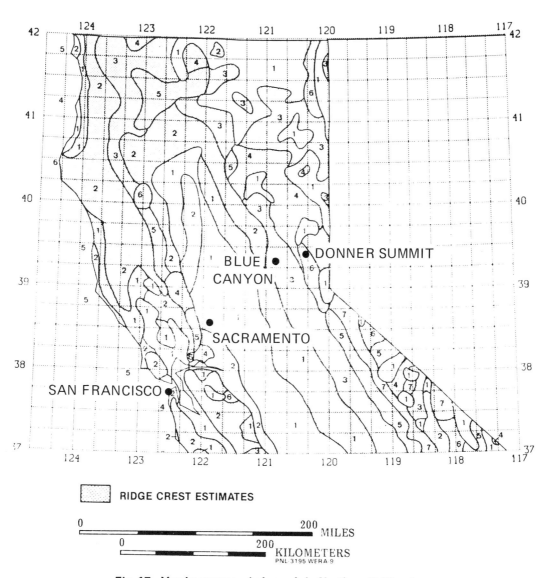

RIDGE CREST ESTIMATES

Fig. 17 Yearly average wind speeds in Northern California.

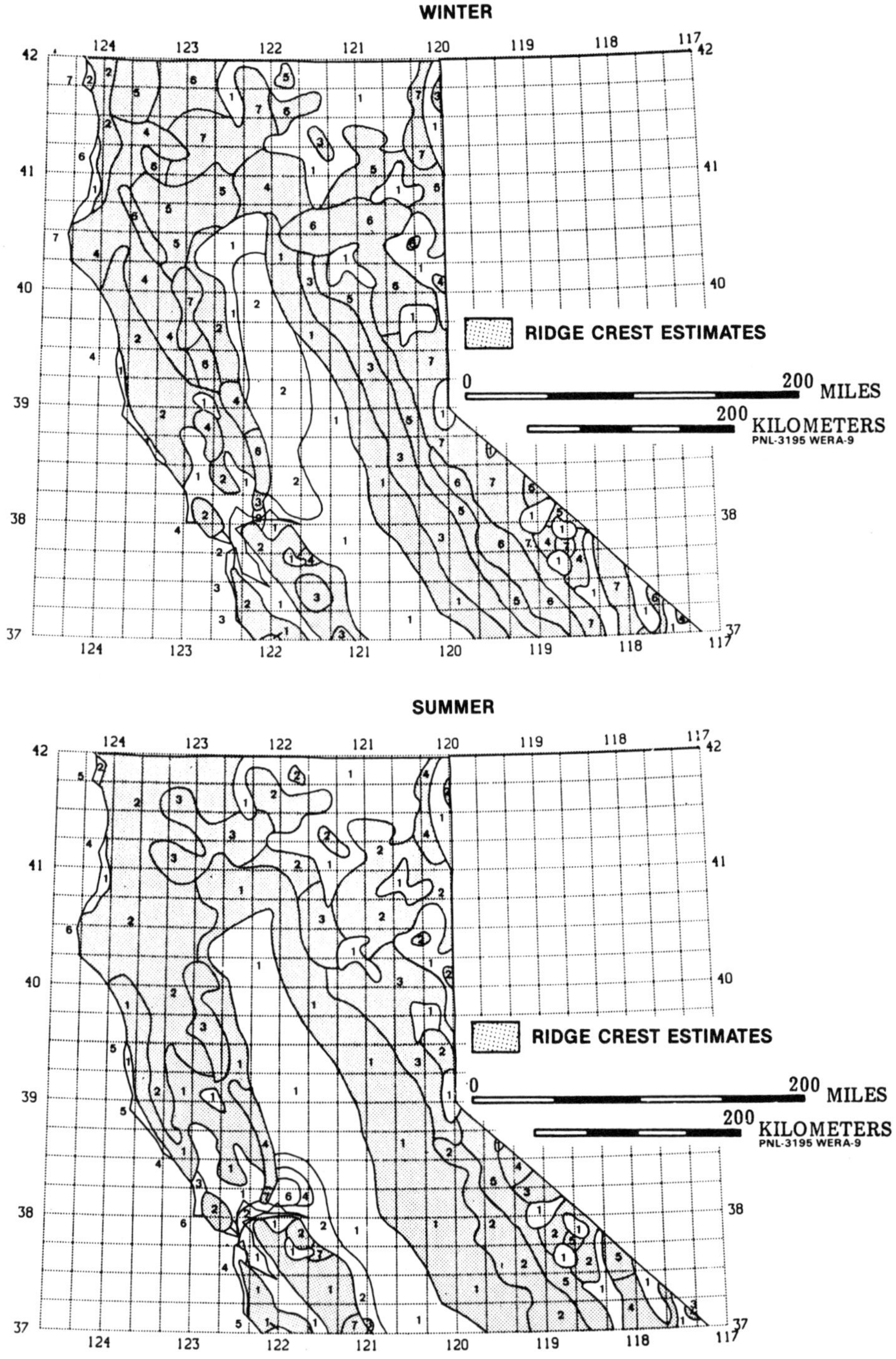

WINTER

SUMMER

AVERAGE YEARLY WIND SPEED (MPH)	CORRESPONDING WIND SPEED CLASS
Below 9.8	1
9.8–11.5	2
11.6–12.5	3
12.6–13.4	4
13.5–14.3	5
14.4–15.7	6
Above 15.7	7

Fig. 18 Seasonal average wind speeds in Northern California.

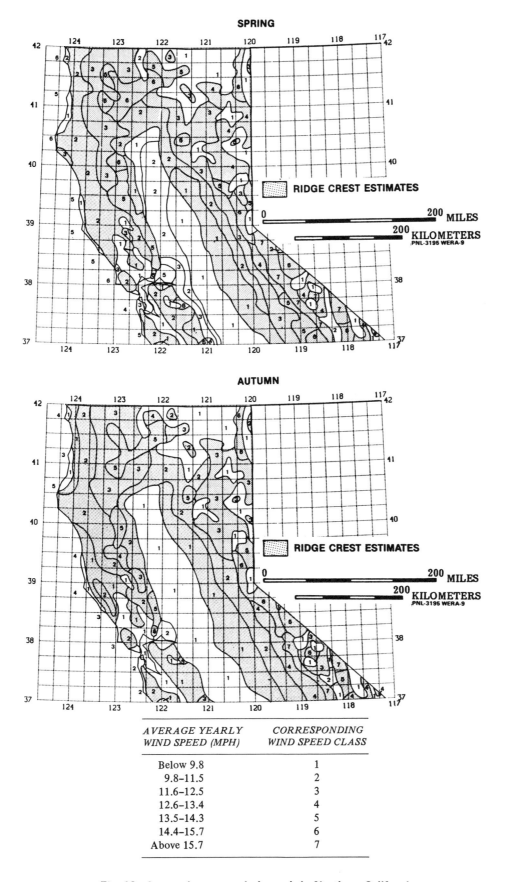

AVERAGE YEARLY WIND SPEED (MPH)	CORRESPONDING WIND SPEED CLASS
Below 9.8	1
9.8–11.5	2
11.6–12.5	3
12.6–13.4	4
13.5–14.3	5
14.4–15.7	6
Above 15.7	7

Fig. 19 Seasonal average wind speeds in Northern California.

average from Class 4 to Class 6. Exposed points along the coast to the north experience Class 6 to Class 7 winds, and Class 3 to Class 4 winds occur along the coast farther south. In the gaps in the Coast Range, speeds are at their lowest of the year but still average between Class 3 and Class 4. Part of the Central Valley experiences Class 2 winds in winter, but the rest of this valley—as well as the plateaus and valleys east of the Sierra Nevada—averages only Class 1 speeds, as it does during other seasons.

Spring brings a slight decrease in wind speed—amounting to about one wind speed class—over most mountain crests. Coastal winds, at exposed points, remain in the Class 4 to Class 6 range, and the Central Valley and other valleys experience about the same average wind speeds as they do during winter. In the wind-energy-rich Coast Range gaps, speeds increase to about Class 6. A region of Class 3 to Class 5 winds extends eastward along the Sacramento River in spring.

During summer, speeds in the Coast Range gaps are about one wind speed class stronger than spring speeds, reaching Class 7 in the windiest places and as high as Class 3 at Stockton and Class 2 at Sacramento in June. Summer winds remain strong offshore (Class 4 to Class 6) but drop to the lightest levels of the year over mountain summits.

Autumn signals a return to winds that are nearly as strong as those of spring on mountain summits but fall off by about one wind speed class in the Coast Range gaps. Wind speeds on the coast are at their lowest of the year during autumn, but are still quite favorable, that is, Class 3 to Class 4. Class 1 speeds prevail throughout the Central Valley and other valleys.

Figure 20 shows the monthly variability of average wind speed at San Francisco, Sacramento, Donner Summit (a pass through the Sierra Nevada Mountains), and Blue Canyon (located east of the Sierra Nevada Mountains). The San Francisco pattern—an early summer peak followed by a winter minimum—is a good example of conditions in the gaps of the Coast Range. The same pattern appears at Sacramento in the Central Valley, although the summer peak there is much lower. Most of the Central Valley does not experience this summer maximum, but rather a weak maximum during early spring.

The seasonal change at Donner Summit reflects conditions over the windy portions of the Sierra Nevada Mountains, that is, the few passes and many high peaks. Winds on the peaks are even stronger than those in the passes. Note that the least windy month at Donner Summit—September (10.8 mph)—is windier than the windiest month at Sacramento—June (10.3 mph).

The small seasonal change in winds at Blue Canyon shows that the massive Sierra Nevada Mountains to the west block the blasts of winter, so that light winds prevail during the entire year. The pattern at Blue Canyon is typical of the region east of the Sierra Nevada Mountains, as well as of most mountain valleys.

AVERAGE WIND SPEEDS BY DAY AND NIGHT

The change in average wind speed over the 24-hour daily cycle at San Francisco, Sacramento, Donner Summit, and Blue Canyon is shown

NORTHERN CALIFONIA

MONTHLY AVERAGE WIND SPEEDS

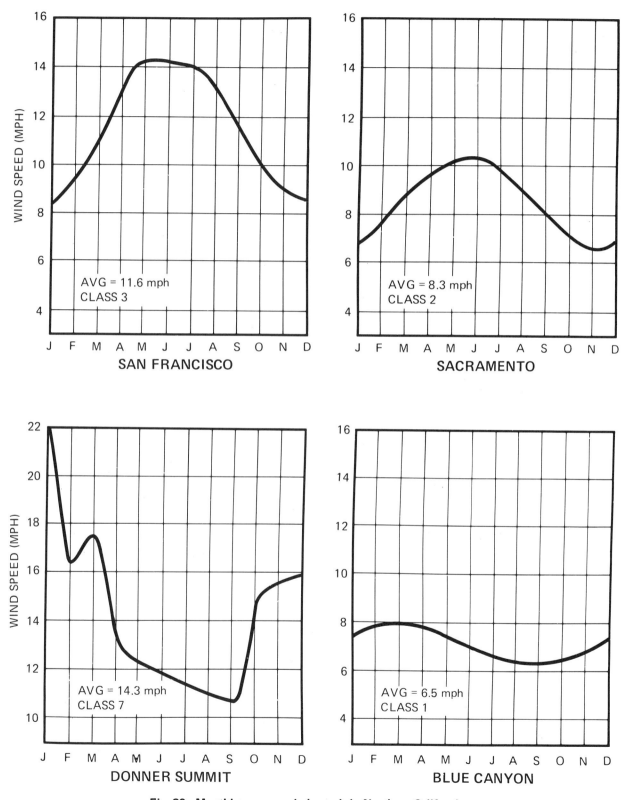

Fig. 20 Monthly average wind speeds in Northern California.

NORTHERN CALIFONIA

HOURLY AVERAGE WIND SPEEDS

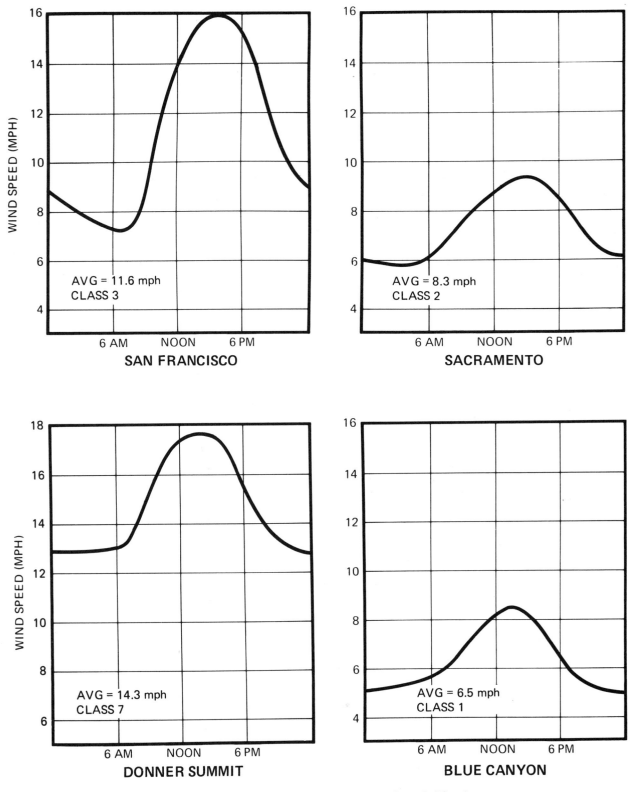

Fig. 21 Hourly average wind speeds in Northern California.

in Fig. 21. The largest day–night variation (9 mph) occurs at San Francisco, where summer winds are nearly twice as strong during the afternoon as they are at sunrise. In summer, the cool ocean air over San Francisco is sucked rapidly eastward by the hot Central Valley, making the hottest time of day the windiest as well in both places. In winter, San Francisco's afternoon winds are scarcely stronger than those at dawn.

In Sacramento, the same midafternoon maximum occurs (most prominently during summer), but the day–night difference (4 mph) is smaller because of Sacramento's distance from San Francisco Bay. Donner Summit is buffeted by winds that average 5 mph stronger during midday than at night; again, the season of greatest day–night change is summer. The winds at Blue Canyon, which is protected by high mountains to the west, are 3 to 4 mph stronger during the early afternoon than they are at midnight. During winter, the day–night difference is only about 1 mph.

Coastal wind speeds change little from day to night whenever the coast is enveloped by fog and mist, as it so often is. When the overcast clears early in the day, however, as it often does in summer, wind speeds often increase rapidly only to fall again as soon as the setting sun beckons the fog and mist to return.

SOUTHERN CALIFORNIA

YEARLY AVERAGE WIND SPEEDS

Strong yearly average wind speeds capable of producing abundant energy from wind machines unfortunately occur in southern California only over some coastal points, mountaintops, and a few mountain passes. In the areas where the most people live—the Los Angeles Basin and the San Joaquin Valley—winds are usually light.

Yearly average wind speeds in southern California are shown in Fig. 22. Along the Pacific Coast, at places exposed to the prevailing northwesterly winds, wind speeds average from Class 4 to Class 5 (12.5–14.3 mph). These places include broad hills and rocky outcrops. The winds over narrow beaches backed by steep cliffs, however, are usually deflected from the beaches by the cliffs. Even over exposed coastal points, rough terrain and forests can rapidly diminish wind speeds as little as a few hundred feet away from the coast. No coastal points southeast of Point Conception experience more than Class 1 winds because the mountains north of the Los Angeles Basin block the prevailing northwest winds. For the same reason, winds are only Class 1 on Santa Catalina and San Clemente Islands and no more than Class 3 on Santa Cruz Island. On exposed portions of San Miguel and Santa Rosa Islands, where winds are not blocked by Point Conception, wind speeds average Class 7.

In the mountains (shaded areas of Fig. 22), winds are usually light in the valleys but stronger on and near the crests; the greater the elevation, the higher the speed. Mountain summits in the low coastal ranges average only Class 2 winds. The Transverse Ranges north of the Los Angeles Basin, the lower ranges of the Sierra Nevada, and most desert ranges average Class 3 to Class 6, whereas the highest part of the Sierra Nevada Mountains and the summits of the ranges east of San Diego average Class 7.

The flat, low-elevation regions of Southern California—where the idyllic climate has attracted millions of people—are protected from the stronger winds passing overhead by the many mountain ranges. The Class 1 winds throughout the Los Angeles Basin, the San Joaquin Valley, and the lower desert are most unsuitable for energy production. Nevertheless, there are windy places not on mountaintops that are accessible to the burgeoning population centers. These are the gaps in the coastal ranges through which cool ocean air flows toward the hot desert. San Gorgonio Pass—located on Interstate 10 just northwest of Palm Springs—is one of the windiest of these gaps. Since winds there average more than 20 mph, it has become a site for a "wind farm" of several hundred wind machines that produce large amounts of electricity for the direct use of consumers. Other gaps where winds are quite strong include Cajon Pass (north of San Bernardino) and Cahonwood Pass (east of Hollister). Another windy area that is not mountainous is near Lancaster, about 50 miles north of Los Angeles.

AVERAGE YEARLY WIND SPEED (MPH)	CORRESPONDING WIND SPEED CLASS
Below 9.8	1
9.8–11.5	2
11.6–12.5	3
12.6–13.4	4
13.5–14.3	5
14.4–15.7	6
Above 15.7	7

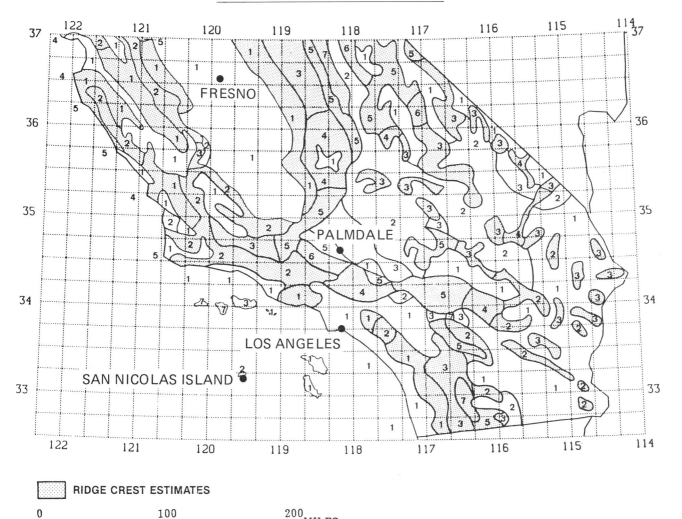

RIDGE CREST ESTIMATES

PNL-3195 WERA-9

Fig. 22 Yearly average wind speeds in Southern California.

SEASONAL AVERAGE WIND SPEEDS

Over the populated valleys of Southern California and most of the desert, the strongest winds blow in spring. Winter is the windiest season in the mountains. Average wind speeds for winter and summer are shown in Fig. 23 and for spring and autumn in Fig. 24. The general pattern of stronger winds along exposed coastal points, through gaps in the Coast Range, and over mountain summits persists during all seasons.

In the mountains, winter is windiest, summer is much less windy, and spring and autumn are about halfway between. Coastal winds vary only slightly but are weakest in autumn (Class 3 to Class 4 north of Pt. Conception) and strongest in spring (Class 5 to Class 6 north of Pt. Conception). South of Pt. Conception, speeds are Class 1 year-round.

In the Coast Range gaps, winds are at their strongest during spring (Class 7). Spring also brings Class 4 to Class 5 winds eastward across the Antelope Valley, from about Lancaster to east of Barstow. Gap speeds are nearly as high in summer as in spring but drop to Class 5, at the most, during winter, the least windy season.

The change in monthly average wind speeds at Los Angeles, San Nicolas Island, Fresno, and Palmdale Airport (near Lancaster) is shown in Fig. 25. The highest speeds come in summer at Fresno, this being the typical pattern of the San Joaquin Valley. Winter speeds at Fresno average only 3 mph lower than summer speeds. At Los Angeles, the peak, if it can be called that, comes in spring, but amounts to only 2 mph more than the light speeds of summer. The Los Angeles graph is typical of wind conditions over most of the Los Angeles Basin and the coastal areas south of Pt. Conception. Wind speeds on San Nicolas Island are typical of those on hilltops of San Miguel and Santa Rosa Islands and coastal points north of Pt. Conception. The April peak is nearly 5 mph greater than the minimum speed, which occurs in October during an average year. The seasonal difference is greatest (6 mph) at Palmdale Airport, where several wind streams meet after crossing adjacent mountain ranges. The seasonal pattern at Palmdale is indicative of that in the San Gorgonio Pass and the other coastal gaps.

AVERAGE WIND SPEEDS BY DAY AND NIGHT

Figure 26 shows the changes in average wind speed from day to night at Los Angeles, San Nicolas Island, Fresno, and Palmdale Airport (near Lancaster). Speeds are highest in midafternoon and lowest from midnight to sunrise at each of these locations. The greatest differences occur at Palmdale Airport (9 mph) and Los Angeles (6 mph). Large increases in daytime speed are typical of the coastal gaps. The day–night difference is only about 2 mph at San Nicolas Island, which is typical of exposed coastal areas, and Fresno, where winds are blocked by nearby mountains.

WINTER

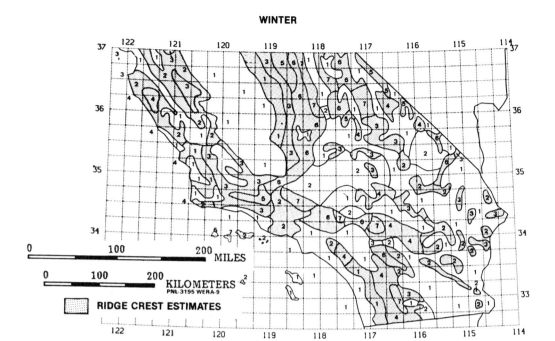

SUMMER

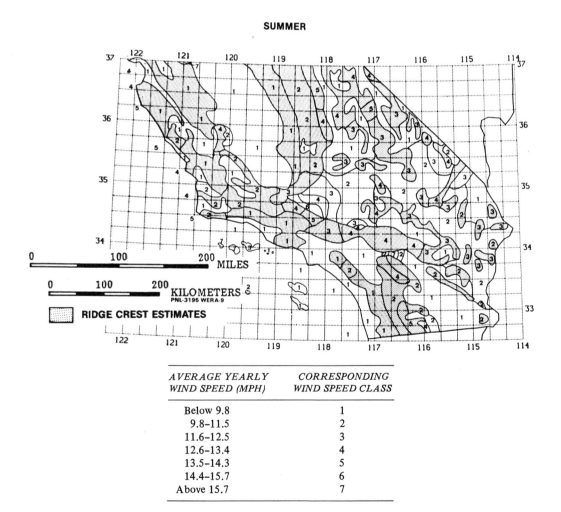

AVERAGE YEARLY WIND SPEED (MPH)	CORRESPONDING WIND SPEED CLASS
Below 9.8	1
9.8–11.5	2
11.6–12.5	3
12.6–13.4	4
13.5–14.3	5
14.4–15.7	6
Above 15.7	7

Fig. 23 Seasonal average wind speeds in Southern California.

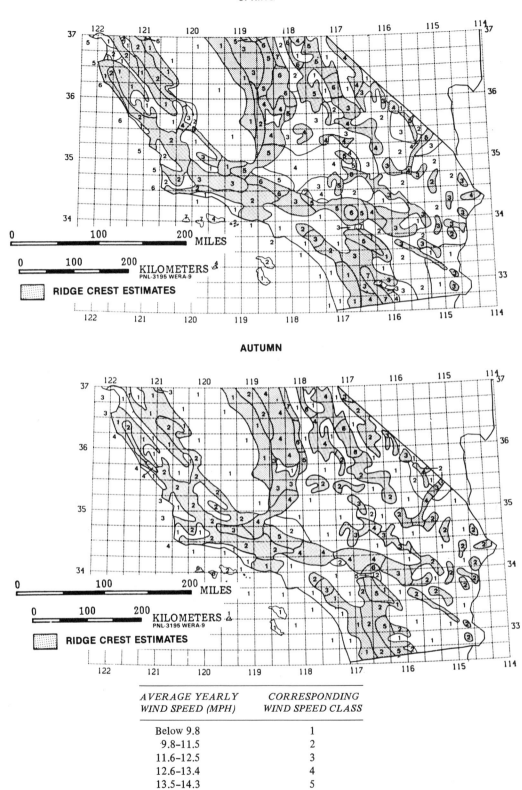

AVERAGE YEARLY WIND SPEED (MPH)	CORRESPONDING WIND SPEED CLASS
Below 9.8	1
9.8–11.5	2
11.6–12.5	3
12.6–13.4	4
13.5–14.3	5
14.4–15.7	6
Above 15.7	7

Fig. 24   Seasonal average wind speeds in Southern California.

SOUTHERN CALIFONIA

MONTHLY AVERAGE WIND SPEEDS

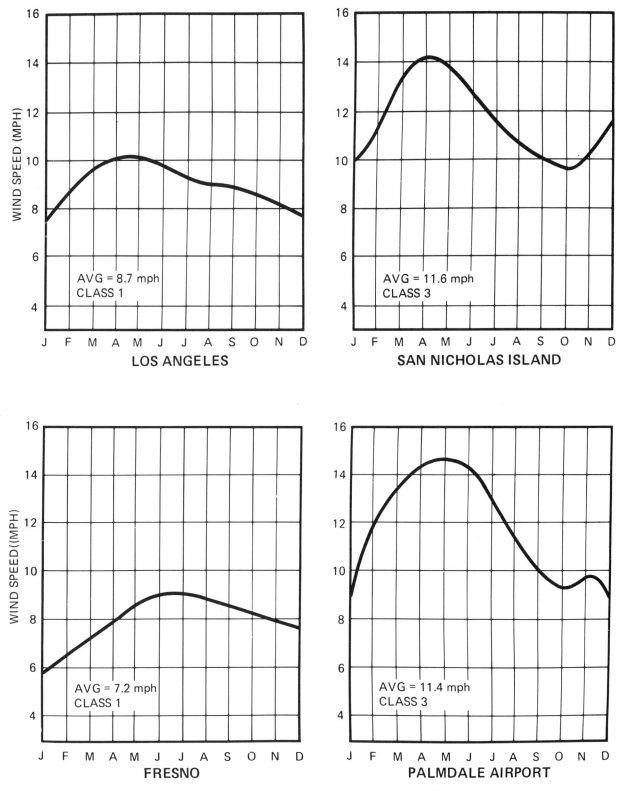

Fig. 25 Monthly average wind speeds in Southern California.

SOUTHERN CALIFONIA

HOURLY AVERAGE WIND SPEEDS

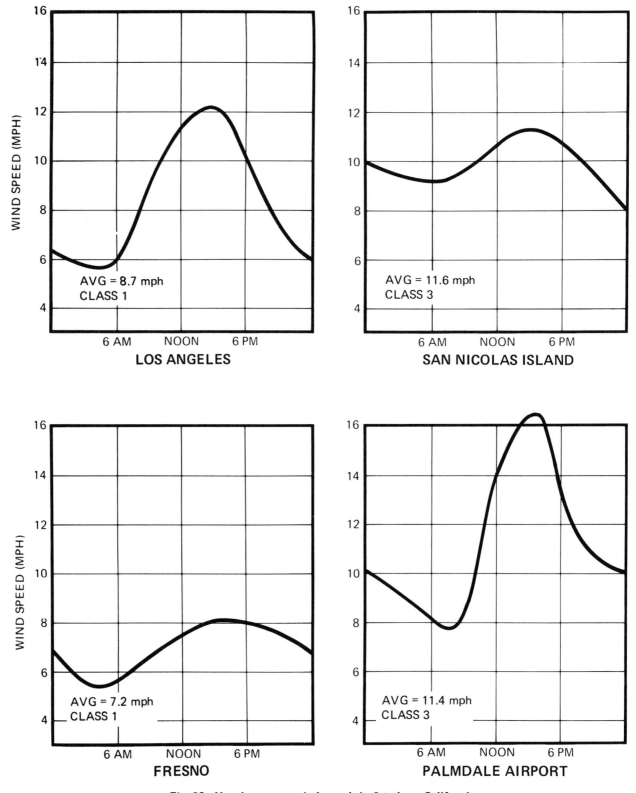

Fig. 26   Hourly average wind speeds in Southern California.

NEVADA

YEARLY AVERAGE WIND SPEEDS

Nevada is made up of a large desert broken by narrow, rocky mountain ranges that rise abruptly from the desert floor. The tops of these ranges are windy, but the valleys below, where most of the sparse population lives, are not, being shielded from the winds by the mountains. The most reasonable sites for wind machines are therefore in the mountain passes and in those few valleys where winds are marginally strong enough for the economical generation of energy.

The yearly average wind speed classes in Nevada are shown in Fig. 27. The ridgecrests in the shaded (mountainous) regions have yearly average speeds ranging from Class 2 (9.8–11.5 mph) on the lowest mountaintops to Class 6 (14.3–15.7 mph) on the highest summits. Most mountain ridges are Class 4 or 5. The lower portions of the mountains and the narrow mountain valleys have much lower wind speeds. Although most mountain crests are not easily accessible, strong winds blow in many of the passes, some of which are traversed by roads to connect neighboring valleys. Wind speeds in these passes may approach those on the summits, especially if the mountain range containing the pass is oriented in a north-south direction. Some of the few valleys that are oriented east to west may also experience strong winds, but their existence has not yet been confirmed because wind measurements in this desert state are meager.

The broad basins between the mountains are normally starved for wind because of the surrounding mountains. Yet, Class 2 (or Class 3) wind speeds do occur in isolated basins, for example, those in the north-central part of the state (near Owyhee), in the northeastern part near the Utah border, in a large desolate region in the northwestern corner, and in the Las Vegas Basin. These areas are windy enough to justify measurement of wind speeds at an exposed site to determine whether a wind machine might be useful.

SEASONAL AVERAGE WIND SPEEDS

On the mountain crests and most mountain passes, the windiest season is winter. At lower elevations, however, spring is windiest. Winds are at their lightest over both mountain and valley in the searing heat of summer.

Average wind speeds for winter and summer are shown in Fig. 28 and for spring and autumn in Fig. 29. Speeds are highest on the mountain crests and lowest in the basins during all seasons. In winter, the highest crests—isolated by deep snow and locked in subzero cold—are blasted by Class 7 winds. Most other summits experience Class 5 or Class 6 winds. At the same time, the basins separating the mountains experience only Class 1 winds, except those along the Idaho border, where the winds are Class 2 to Class 3. As spring arrives, mountain crest winds usually decrease by about one class, whereas basin winds rise to Class 2 over most of the state, except in the basins along the Idaho border and in the Las Vegas Basin, where they may reach Class 3.

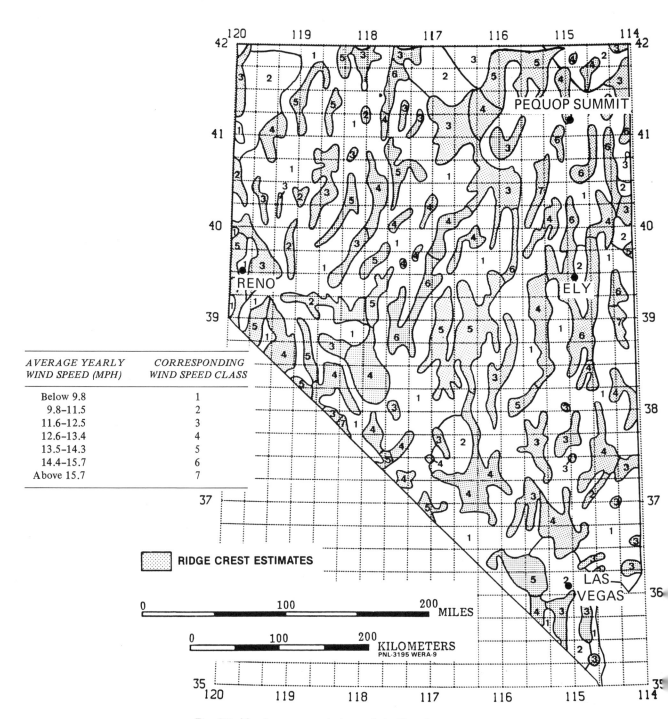

AVERAGE YEARLY WIND SPEED (MPH)	CORRESPONDING WIND SPEED CLASS
Below 9.8	1
9.8–11.5	2
11.6–12.5	3
12.6–13.4	4
13.5–14.3	5
14.4–15.7	6
Above 15.7	7

RIDGE CREST ESTIMATES

PNL-3195 WERA-9

Fig. 27 Yearly average wind speeds in Nevada.

AVERAGE YEARLY WIND SPEED (MPH)	CORRESPONDING WIND SPEED CLASS
Below 9.8	1
9.8–11.5	2
11.6–12.5	3
12.6–13.4	4
13.5–14.3	5
14.4–15.7	6
Above 15.7	7

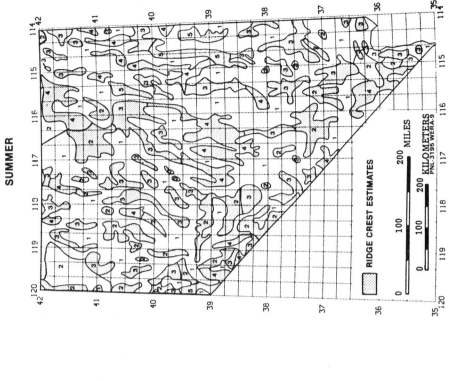

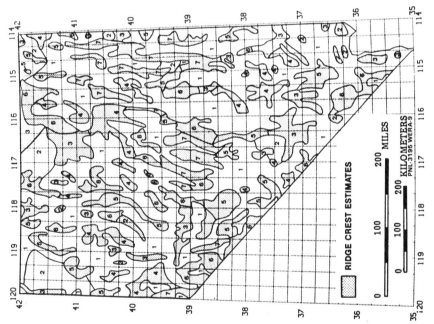

Fig. 28 Seasonal average wind speeds in Nevada.

AVERAGE YEARLY WIND SPEED (MPH)	CORRESPONDING WIND SPEED CLASS
Below 9.8	1
9.8–11.5	2
11.6–12.5	3
12.6–13.4	4
13.5–14.3	5
14.4–15.7	6
Above 15.7	7

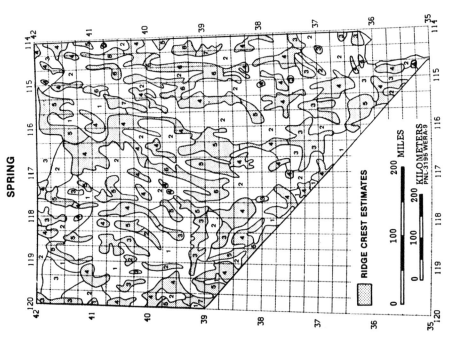

Fig. 29   Seasonal average wind speeds in Nevada.

Summer winds are lower, being no more than Class 5 on the highest mountains and Class 1 in the valleys, except for valleys along the Idaho border and in the Las Vegas Basin, where they are Class 2. Autumn winds on the mountaintops are stronger than summer winds but lighter than spring winds. In the basins, autumn winds are scarcely stronger than the very light winds of summer.

Figure 30 shows the change of monthly average wind speeds at Las Vegas, Reno, Pequop Summit (a typical mountain pass, on Rt. 80 about 50 miles east of Elko), and Ely (in a narrow valley in the eastern part of the state). At the three low-elevation stations—Las Vegas, Reno and Ely—wind speeds are highest in April and lowest in December. At Ely, the average change throughout the year amounts to only about 1 mph, but at Las Vegas and Reno the difference between the windiest and least windy month is about 3 mph. Pequop Summit has very strong winds during winter (over 18 mph) and the lightest winds in September (11.5 mph).

AVERAGE WIND SPEEDS BY DAY AND NIGHT

Wind speeds are normally stronger during the day than at night, and Nevada's winds are no exception. The average change in wind speed from day to night at Las Vegas, Reno, Ely, and Pequop Summit is shown in Fig. 31.

The highest speeds occur during the afternoon at all four of these locations. At Pequop Summit, the peak comes just after high noon. In some mountain passes and on mountain tops, the highest winds may come at any time of the day or even at night. Speeds are at their highest at Las Vegas and Ely about midafternoon and at Reno in late afternoon. The lowest speeds occur near sunrise at all four locations. The day-to-night difference amounts to nearly 5 mph at Reno, 4 mph at Pequop Summit, 3 mph at Ely, and 2 mph at Las Vegas. The daily cycle is most pronounced during spring and summer, particularly at the lower elevations.

NEVADA

MONTHLY AVERAGE WIND SPEEDS

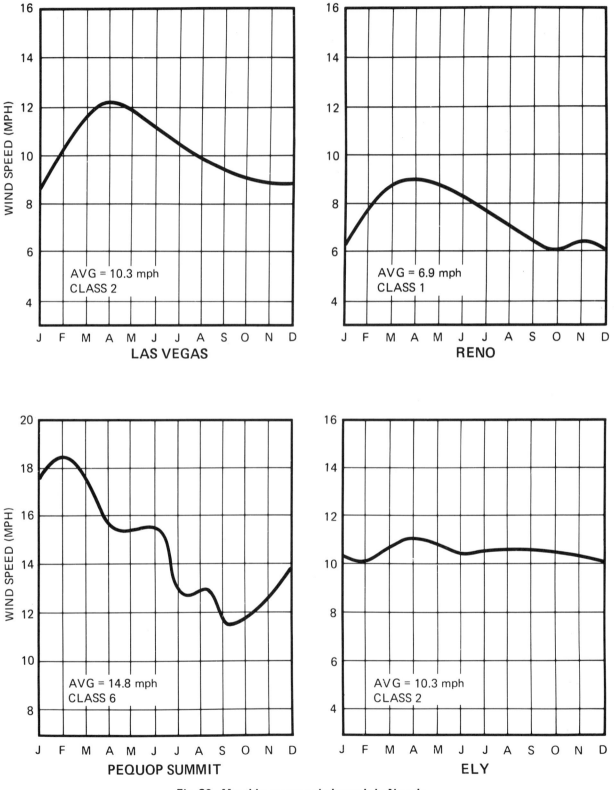

Fig. 30 Monthly average wind speeds in Nevada.

NEVADA

HOURLY AVERAGE WIND SPEEDS

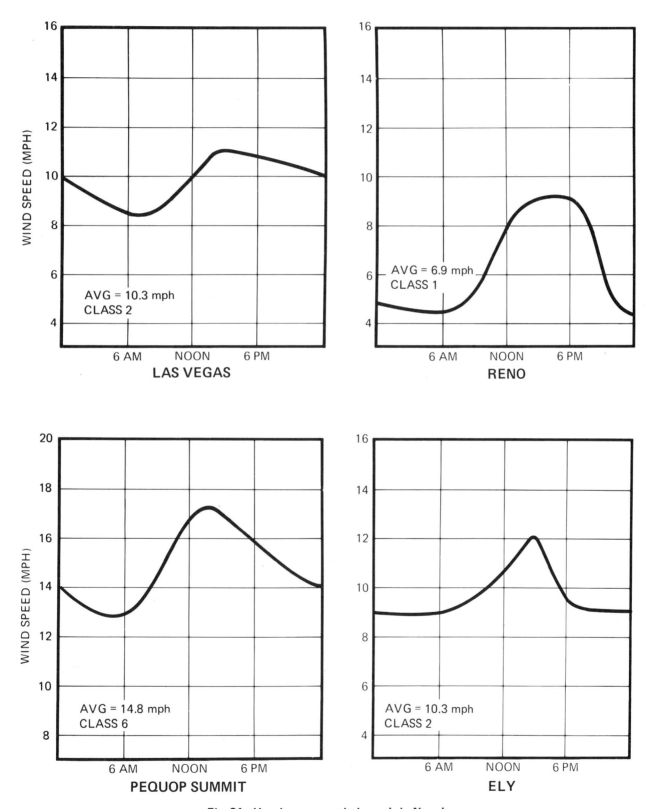

Fig. 31 Hourly average wind speeds in Nevada.

WIND SPEED AND WIND POWER AT VARIOUS LOCATIONS IN CALIFORNIA AND NEVADA

The table that follows shows the yearly average wind speed and the yearly average wind power at each location in California and Nevada where winds are measured frequently and reliably. Not enough measurements have been made at other locations to provide the basis for computing reliable yearly averages. (For a definition of wind power and its relationship to average wind speed, refer to page 3.)

WIND SPEED AND WIND POWER AT VARIOUS LOCATIONS IN CALIFORNIA AND NEVADA

TOWN, CITY, OR PLACE	FACILITY	YEARLY AVERAGE WIND SPEED (MPH AT 33 FT ABOVE GROUND)	YEARLY AVERAGE WIND POWER (WATTS PER SQ. METER)
	NORTHERN CALIFORNIA		
Arcata	Arcata Airport	6.7	59
Marysville	Beale Air Force Base	5.8	68
Bishop	Bishop Airport	9.9	101
Blue Canyon	Blue Canyon Airport	6.5	43
Crescent City	Crescent City Airport	9.9	178
Donner Summit	Donner Summit CAA	14.3	401
Fairfield	Travis Air Force Base	11.6	209
Merced	Castle Air Force Base	5.8	50
Montague	Siskiyou County Airport	7.8	88
Mt. Shasta City	Mt. Shasta Weather Bureau Office	6.5	30
Oakland	Oakland Airport	9.4	89
Red Bluff	Red Bluff Airport	9.2	103
Sacramento	Sacramento Airport	8.3	72
San Francisco	San Francisco Airport	11.6	177
San Rafael	Hamilton Air Force Base	6.0	52
Stockton	Stockton Airport	9.4	84
Sunnyvale	Moffet Naval Air Station	5.8	45
Ukiah	Ukiah Airport	4.0	28
	SOUTHERN CALIFORNIA		
Bakersfield	Bakersfield Airport	7.6	45
China Lake	China Lake Naval Air Facility	7.6	107
Daggett	Daggett Airport	12.1	197
El Centro	El Centro Naval Auxiliary Air Station	8.5	92
Fresno	Fresno Air Terminal	7.2	37
In-Ko-Pah Gorge	Desert View Tower	18.0	547
Los Angeles	Los Angeles International Airport	8.7	64
Mt. Laguna	Mt. Laguna CAA	22.0	1579
Needles	Needles Airport	8.5	98
Palmdale	Palmdale Airport	11.4	188
Paso Robles	Paso Robles Airport	6.7	64
Riverside	March Air Force Base	4.9	40
Salinas	Salinas Airport	9.0	89
Sandberg	Sandberg Airport	13.2	209

TOWN, CITY, OR PLACE	FACILITY	YEARLY AVERAGE WIND SPEED (MPH AT 33 FT ABOVE GROUND)	YEARLY AVERAGE WIND POWER (WATTS PER SQ. METER)
SOUTHERN CALIFORNIA (continued)			
San Diego	San Diego International Airport	7.8	41
San Nicolas Island	San Nicolas Naval Facility	11.6	199
Thermal	Thermal Airport	8.7	74
Vandenberg	Vandenberg Air Force Base	7.6	81
NEVADA			
Battle Mountain	Battle Mountain Airport	9.2	94
Elko	Elko Airport	6.1	45
Ely	Ely Airport	10.3	106
Fallon	Fallon Naval Auxiliary Air Station	5.4	36
Las Vegas	McCarran International Airport	10.3	124
Lovelock	Lovelock Airport	6.7	66
Pequop Summit	Bonneville Power Administration Facility	14.8	326
Reno	Reno International Airport	6.9	66
Tonapah	Tonapah Airport	10.1	99
Winnemucca	Winnemucca Airport	8.7	63
Yucca Flat	Yucca Flat Weather Bureau Office	7.4	71

4
Southwestern States

- Utah
- Arizona
- Colorado
- New Mexico

GENERAL INFORMATION

Wind speeds in the southwestern states are favorable for the production of energy by wind machines in the eastern plains of Colorado and New Mexico, atop many mountain ridges, and in a few of the basins and passes separating mountain ranges. In the broad basins and plains immediately adjacent to the Rocky Mountains, however —which is the region where the most people live—wind speeds are usually too light for wind machines to be economical. Of the four states, Arizona has the fewest good sites for wind machines. The yearly average wind speeds in this region are shown in Fig. 32.

Since the mountains affect wind speeds so drastically, it is worth noting major ranges, where wind speeds are highest. These include the Uinta Mountains of northeastern Utah, the Wasatch Range in central Utah, the San Juan Range in southwestern Colorado, and the Sangre de Cristo Mountains of southern Colorado and northern New Mexico. Some other ranges in the region are nearly as high and as windy but cover a much smaller area. The tops of the smaller ranges and the numerous tablelands have stronger winds than the basins, but these winds are lighter than those in the higher mountains. The winds are light in most mountain valleys.

Average wind speeds increase eastward from the Rocky Mountains toward the eastern borders of Colorado and New Mexico. On these flat, treeless plains, there is little to block the free flow of the wind, which therefore averages moderate to strong.

The seasons of strongest wind are shown in Fig. 33. Spring is the windiest season on the plains and the broad basins between the mountains except for those in the extreme northern parts of Colorado and northeastern Utah, where winter is windiest. Spring is also the windiest season on the mountain ridges of Arizona and southwestern New Mexico, but winter is windiest on the tops of the mountains of Colorado, Utah, and northeastern New Mexico.

AVERAGE YEARLY WIND SPEED (MPH)	CORRESPONDING WIND SPEED CLASS
Below 9.8	1
9.8–11.5	2
11.6–12.5	3
12.6–13.4	4
13.5–14.3	5
14.4–15.7	6
Above 15.7	7

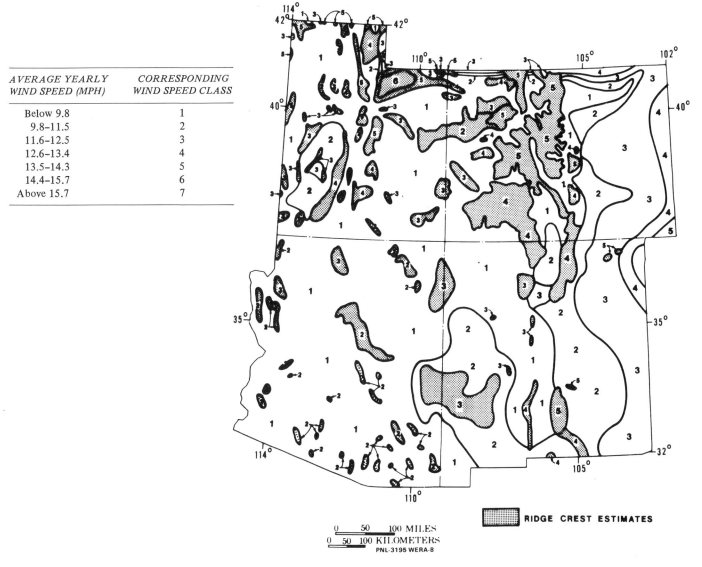

Fig. 32 Yearly average wind speeds in the Southwest.

AVERAGE YEARLY WIND SPEED (MPH)	CORRESPONDING WIND SPEED CLASS
Below 9.8	1
9.8–11.5	2
11.6–12.5	3
12.6–13.4	4
13.5–14.3	5
14.4–15.7	6
Above 15.7	7

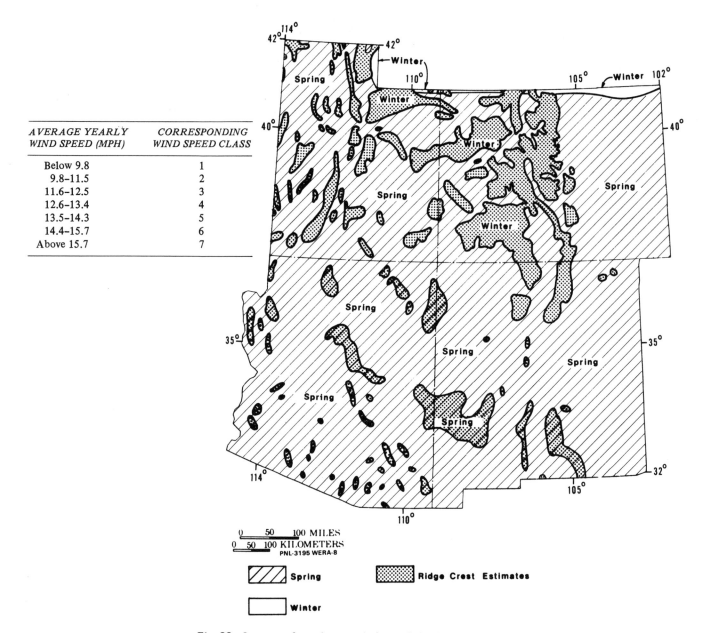

Fig. 33 Seasons of maximum wind speeds in the Southwest.

UTAH

YEARLY AVERAGE WIND SPEEDS

The only regions of strong winds in Utah are atop the highest mountains and ridges. Moderate winds blow over the broad basin in the southwestern part of the state and near the Wyoming border.

Utah's yearly average wind speeds are shown in Fig. 34. The remote crests of the Uinta Mountains—the highest in the state—experience Class 5 to Class 6 winds (13.4–15.7 mph). Class 5 winds are also found atop the northern part of the Wasatch Range and on a few peaks of the Deep Creek and Grouse Creek Mountains in the northwest. Some mountain passes may have winds that approach the speeds of those on the crests. Other mountain ridges have average speeds of Class 3 or Class 4. Such windy places are often quite difficult to get to and are subject to heavy snow and icing during much of the year. The lower slopes and valleys between the mountains have much lower average wind speeds.

An extensive area of fairly level land in the southwestern part of the state—an area bounded by the Wasatch and Wah Wah Mountains on the east and west, Zion National Park on the south, and the town of Delta on the north—provides Class 2 and Class 3 winds, which are marginally sufficient for the economical generation of energy by wind machines. Additional regions of moderate winds probably exist between other mountain ranges in western Utah, but few wind measurements have been made and it is impossible to know just where these regions are located or how strongly winds blow in them. At locations in the broad basins between the mountain ranges where measurements have been recorded, only Class 1 winds have been found.

The Logan–Salt Lake City–Provo "megalopolis" falls within this area of Class 1 winds. There are indications, however, that the canyons just east of Ogden and Salt Lake City experience at least moderate winds. Strong winds have been known to blow at least briefly in these canyons while the air remained quite calm in the urban areas just to their west.

SEASONAL AVERAGE WIND SPEEDS

The seasonal pattern of average wind speeds in Utah is shown by the winter and summer maps (Fig. 35) and the spring and autumn maps (Fig. 36). Mountain crest winds are strongest in winter; basin winds, during spring. On mountain tops, the least windy season is summer; in the basins, it is autumn.

Winter speeds are Class 7 on the upper peaks of the Uinta and northern Wasatch Mountains. Class 5 to Class 6 winds blow on mountaintops of moderate height and Class 3 to Class 4 winds on the lower mountains and rougher plateaus. In most basins, winds are only Class 1, the exception being the southwestern part of the state centered near Milford where they are either Class 2 or Class 3.

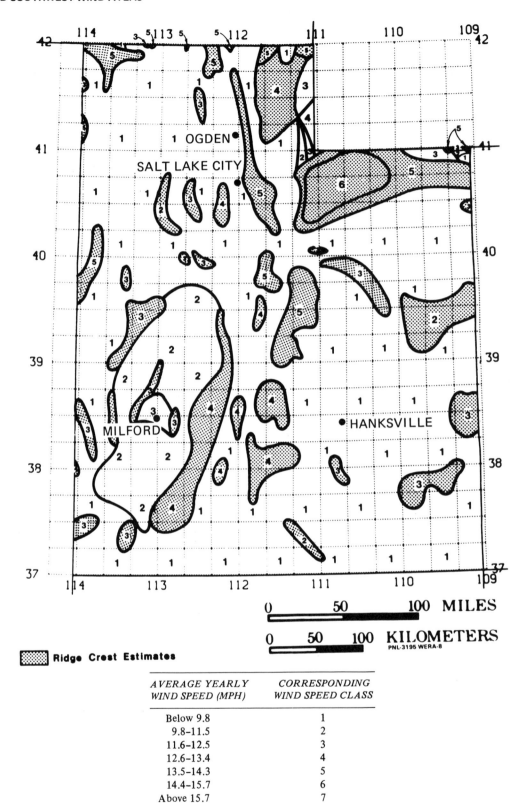

Ridge Crest Estimates

AVERAGE YEARLY WIND SPEED (MPH)	CORRESPONDING WIND SPEED CLASS
Below 9.8	1
9.8–11.5	2
11.6–12.5	3
12.6–13.4	4
13.5–14.3	5
14.4–15.7	6
Above 15.7	7

Fig. 34   Yearly average wind speeds in Utah.

As spring approaches, winds decrease by about one wind speed class on mountain ridges but increase by one class in the basins. Speeds near Milford reach their peak of the year—Class 4—during the spring season. Summer brings a further drop of two to three classes on mountaintops, and the area of moderate winds in the southwestern basin shrinks back to about its size in winter. In autumn, wind speeds are at their lightest of the year over the basins and valleys but increase by one to two classes on the mountaintops.

The change in monthly average wind speeds at Salt Lake City, Ogden, Hanksville (in the southeast), and Milford (near the center of the region of moderate winds in the southwest) is shown in Fig. 37. Speeds change little through the year at Salt Lake City and Ogden, being no more than about 2 mph stronger in March and April than in November and December. The springtime wind speed maximum is quite noticeable at Hanksville, the winds there being very light from July through February. At Milford, winds are comparatively strong throughout the year, averaging nearly 14 mph from March through August.

AVERAGE WIND SPEEDS BY DAY AND NIGHT

In general, the highest wind speeds in Utah occur during the afternoon and the lowest at night. In some places, the difference between day and night speeds is quite large (7 mph, or more), and in others it is hardly noticeable. Open areas far from mountains usually reveal a moderate day-to-night difference, whereas in areas close to mountain ranges the difference may be either large or small. The daily pattern at most locations can be determined only by measurement. On mountaintops, the range of speeds is often small, and it may even be windier at night than during the day. At almost all locations, the day-to-night change is greatest during spring and summer and usually very small in winter.

The 24-hour change in average wind speeds at Salt Lake City, Ogden, Hanksville, and Milford is shown in Fig. 38. At each location, the lowest speed occurs near sunrise and the peak between noon and 5 P.M. The day-and-night difference at Salt Lake City and Ogden is only 2 to 3 mph, at Hanksville 6 mph, and at Milford 7 mph.

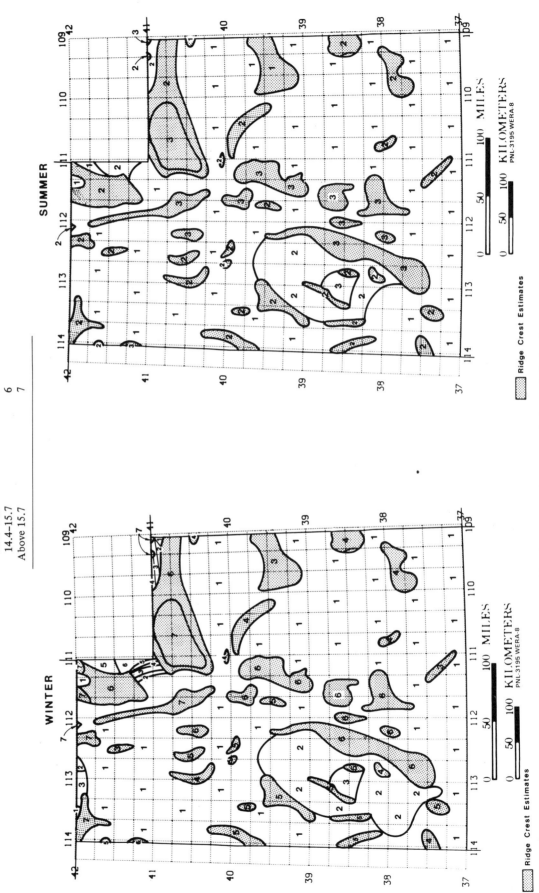

AVERAGE YEARLY WIND SPEED (MPH)	CORRESPONDING WIND SPEED CLASS
Below 9.8	1
9.8–11.5	2
11.6–12.5	3
12.6–13.4	4
13.5–14.3	5
14.4–15.7	6
Above 15.7	7

Fig. 35   Seasonal average wind speeds in Utah.

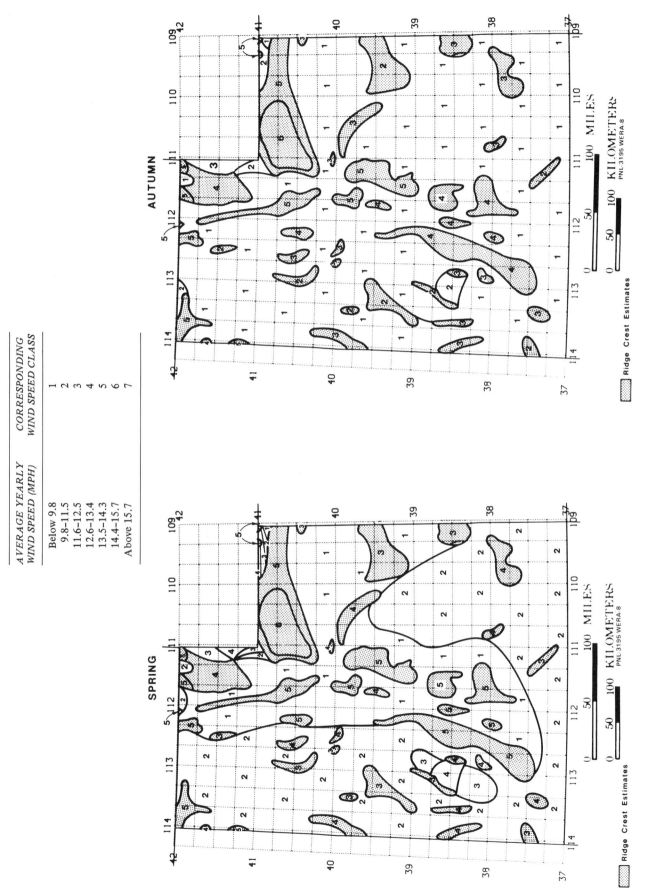

Fig. 36 Seasonal average wind speeds in Utah.

UTAH

MONTHLY AVERAGE WIND SPEEDS

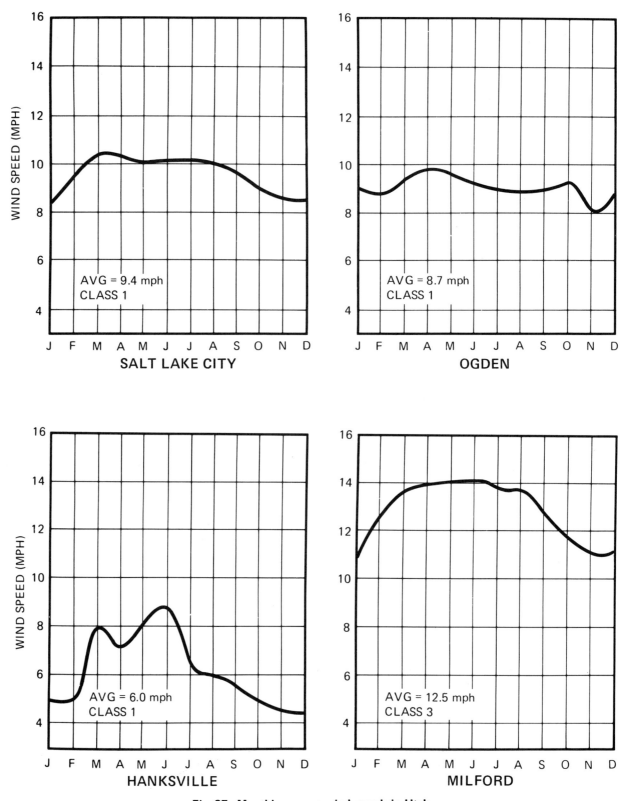

Fig. 37 Monthly average wind speeds in Utah.

UTAH

HOURLY AVERAGE WIND SPEEDS

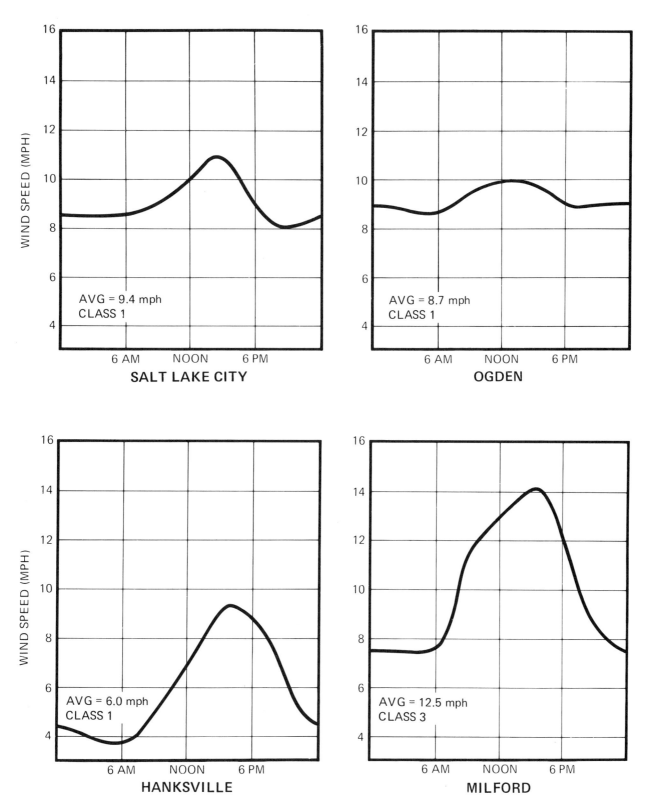

Fig. 38 Hourly average wind speeds in Utah.

COLORADO

YEARLY AVERAGE WIND SPEEDS

Wind speeds in Colorado are favorable for energy production by wind machines over some parts of the eastern plains and atop the high, but frequently remote, mountains. At the base of the Rockies, where the majority of the population lives, and within most mountain valleys and basins, only a few sites have relatively favorable wind speeds.

A map of yearly average wind speeds in Colorado is shown in Fig. 39. Winds average Class 4 to Class 5 (12.5–14.3 mph) on the peaks and ridges of the many high mountains (shaded areas of Fig. 39), including those in the Front, Gore, Sangre de Cristo, and San Juan ranges. Speeds average Class 2 to Class 3 atop the lower ranges and plateaus in the extreme west. The lower mountain slopes and mountain valleys, as well as the broad basins between the mountains, usually have only Class 1 winds. Exceptions are as follows: (1) part of the San Luis Valley (in the south-central part of the state), where winds average Class 2, and (2) along the Wyoming border, where Class 3 winds prevail.

Immediately to the east of the Rocky Mountains—in the region where the growing cities of Greeley, Ft. Collins, Denver, Boulder, Colorado Springs, Pueblo, and Trinidad are located—wind speeds average only Class 1 or 2 because the prevailing westerly winds are blocked by the mountains. The Class 1 winds extend eastward down the South Platte River Valley nearly as far as Sterling. Elsewhere, winds increase to Class 3 over the very sparsely populated plains to the east, reaching Class 4 near the Kansas border and even Class 5 in the extreme southeast. The plains offer ideal locations for wind machines, not only because of the strong winds, but because of the nearly level terrain and scarcity of trees.

SEASONAL AVERAGE WIND SPEEDS

Wind speeds rise and fall with the changing seasons over the entire state. The change is greatest over the mountain tops and least in the mountain valleys and western basins. Average wind speeds for winter and summer are shown in Fig. 40 and for spring and autumn in Fig. 41.

Winter is the season of strongest winds over the remote high mountain ridges. Here, Class 6 to Class 7 winds howl over towering ranges, buried under many feet of snow, and Class 3 to Class 5 winds assault the lower westernmost ranges and plateaus. Yet in the mountain valleys and basins—protected by the steep mountainsides—the air lies cold and calm much of the time, resulting in only Class 1 winds. Very near the Wyoming border, powerful westerly winds rushing through the only sizable gap in the northern Rockies can be as strong as Class 5. For the same reason, winter speeds can be as high as Class 6 east of the mountain front and just south of Wyoming's southeastern corner. Class 4 to Class 5 winds are found along the Kansas border, but the blocking effect of the huge rampart of the Rockies results in

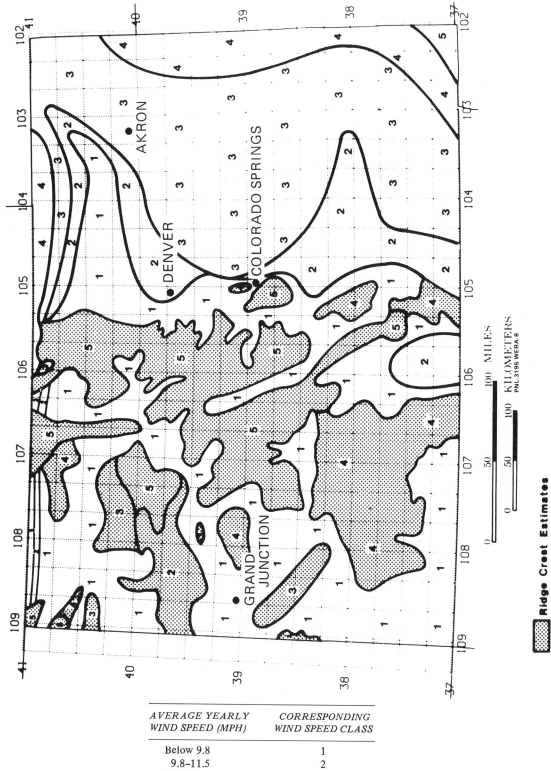

Fig. 39 Yearly average wind speeds in Colorado.

Ridge Crest Estimates

AVERAGE YEARLY WIND SPEED (MPH)	CORRESPONDING WIND SPEED CLASS
Below 9.8	1
9.8–11.5	2
11.6–12.5	3
12.6–13.4	4
13.5–14.3	5
14.4–15.7	6
Above 15.7	7

WINTER

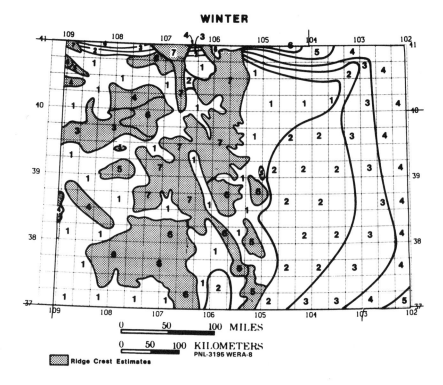

AVERAGE YEARLY WIND SPEED (MPH)	CORRESPONDING WIND SPEED CLASS
Below 9.8	1
9.8–11.5	2
11.6–12.5	3
12.6–13.4	4
13.5–14.3	5
14.4–15.7	6
Above 15.7	7

SUMMER

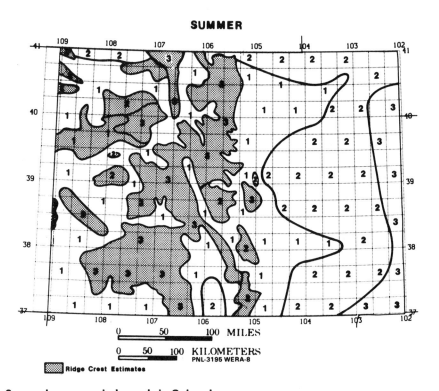

Fig. 40   Seasonal average wind speeds in Colorado.

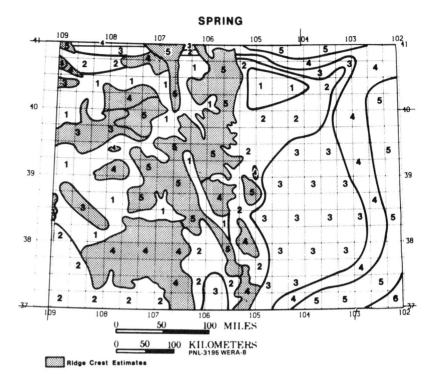

AVERAGE YEARLY	*CORRESPONDING*
WIND SPEED (MPH)	*WIND SPEED CLASS*
Below 9.8	1
9.8–11.5	2
11.6–12.5	3
12.6–13.4	4
13.5–14.3	5
14.4–15.7	6
Above 15.7	7

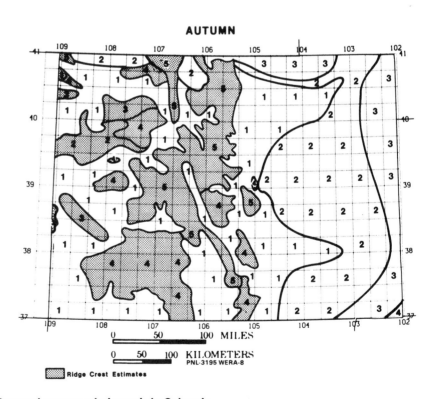

Fig. 41 Seasonal average wind speeds in Colorado.

only Class 1 speeds over Colorado's embryonic megalopolis—Greeley–Denver–Pueblo.

When stronger winds do blow immediately east of the Rockies, they sometimes gather destructive force. These famous and fierce Chinook winds, with velocities of 50 to over 100 mph in some cases, temper winter's cold but are hardly conducive to the use of wind machines.

With the arrival of spring, winds abate by one or two classes on the mountain ridges and increase to Class 2 over some of the broad western basins. Winds on the plains are stronger in spring than at any other time of year. Over most of the populous strip at the foot of the Rockies, spring is the only season in which they become as strong as Class 2, but Class 4 to Class 5 winds blow over a broad band of easternmost Colorado and reach Class 6 over the southeastern corner. Class 5 speeds also are found along the Wyoming border.

Summer and autumn are the seasons of least wind. During summer, speeds can be as high as Class 3 only atop the highest peaks and close to the Kansas border. Class 5 winds blow on the remote mountain ridges during autumn, but autumn winds on the plains are only marginally stronger than those of summer. Speeds in the mountain valleys and basins are only Class 1 during both seasons.

The change in monthly average wind speed at four Colorado locations—Denver, Colorado Springs, Akron, and Grand Junction—is shown in Fig. 42. The windiest month is either March or April at Denver, Akron, and Colorado Springs, but June is windiest at Grand Junction. The season of lightest winds is autumn at the first three locations and midwinter at Grand Junction. Denver and Colorado Springs have seasonal wind patterns typical of those found at the foot of the Rockies. Akron is representative of seasonal changes on the open plains, and the seasonal pattern at Grand Junction differs little from that of the many mountain valleys and basins throughout the rest of the state.

AVERAGE WIND SPEEDS BY DAY AND NIGHT

The usual nationwide pattern of highest winds during the day and lowest at night holds true in Colorado. The hourly change in average wind speed at Denver, Colorado Springs, Akron, and Grand Junction is shown in Fig. 43. Speeds are lowest near dawn at all locations except Grand Junction, where the minimum occurs about noon. Winds reach their highest levels during midafternoon at all four locations. They are also about 2 to 4 mph stronger at the windiest time of the day than at sunrise, with the exception of Grand Junction again, where the day-to-night difference amounts to only about 1 mph. The small 24-hour change at Grand Junction is not unique but typical of the many valleys where the majority of people who live west of the Continental Divide reside. In these valleys, cold air, which is comparatively heavy, becomes trapped and cannot be warmed and dislodged for movement until the sun is at its strongest.

At all locations, the day-to-night change in winds is greater in spring and summer than in autumn and winter.

COLORADO

MONTHLY AVERAGE WIND SPEEDS

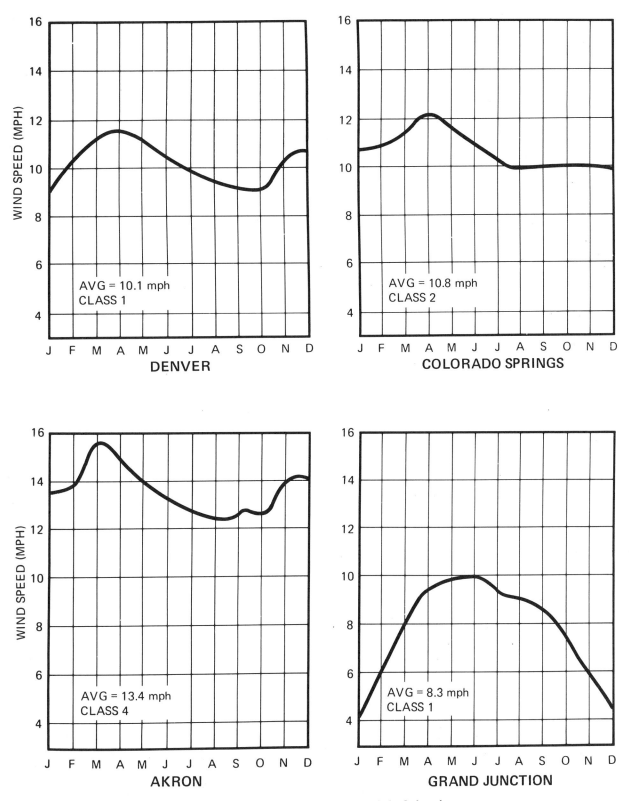

Fig. 42 Monthly average wind speeds in Colorado.

COLORADO

HOURLY AVERAGE WIND SPEEDS

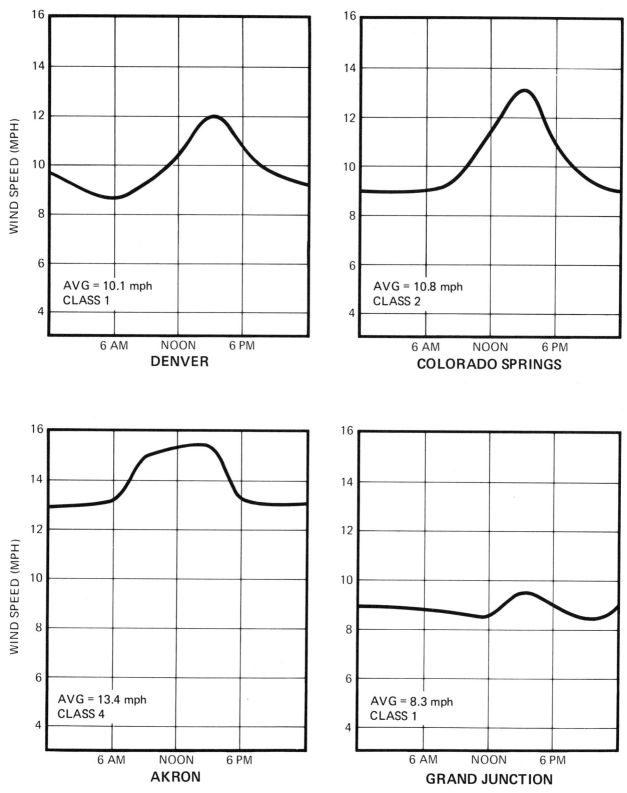

Fig. 43 Hourly average wind speeds in Colorado.

ARIZONA

YEARLY AVERAGE WIND SPEEDS

Favorable sites for wind machines in Arizona are hard to find. The highest mountain ridges and a few mountain passes, valleys, and mesa tops provide marginally useful wind speeds, but over most of the lower desert, where the majority of people live, the speeds are too light for economical operation of even the most advanced wind machines.

The yearly average wind speeds for the state are shown in Fig. 44. The mountainous (shaded) areas stand out as virtually the only ones in which wind speeds reach a higher average than Class 1, that is, higher than 9.8 mph. Chief among these mountains are the Mogollon Rim, the San Francisco and White Mountains, various mesas in the northeast, and a number of small, narrow ranges scattered over the south and west. Atop the highest ridges and mesas in the northeast, winds attain a modest Class 3 status, but over the San Francisco Mountains and the smaller ranges, they are only Class 2. In the mountain valleys, they are Class 1.

The gap between two of the smaller mountain ranges near Kingman results in Class 2 winds in that vicinity, and similar Class 2 wind areas may exist in other mountain gaps or passes that have yet to be identified. Class 2 areas are known to exist, however, on the plateau surrounding the White Mountains and various plateaus and mesas in other parts of the state. Otherwise, the winds in all level parts of Arizona average only Class 1.

SEASONAL AVERAGE WIND SPEEDS

Spring is the windiest season throughout Arizona, and either autumn or winter is the least windy. Average wind speeds for winter and summer are shown in Fig. 45, and for spring and autumn in Fig. 46. The strongest winds during spring, as in other seasons, are on the mountain ridges, where speeds average Class 3 to Class 4 on the higher summits and Class 2 on the lower ones. Other Class 3 areas are found in the Kingman vicinity, on the plateau surrounding the White Mountains, and possibly in other mountain gaps and plateaus. Spring is the only season when winds are as strong as Class 2 over the relatively level areas in the northern and central parts of the state, but even then only Class 1 winds are found at the low elevations of the southern part.

During summer, wind speeds average about one class lower than in spring except in the White Mountains, where they drop to Class 1 or 2 from Class 3 or 4. Although the autumn map (Fig. 46) appears nearly identical to the summer map (Fig. 45), autumn winds at most locations are even lighter than summer winds.

Winter is the season of the lightest winds in southern Arizona. Even on mountain ridges they are only Class 1, and average lower speeds at lower elevations—Phoenix, for example—drop to about 4 mph. In northern and central Arizona, winter winds are usually Class 1 at lower elevations but may increase by one or two classes on the higher mountain ridges.

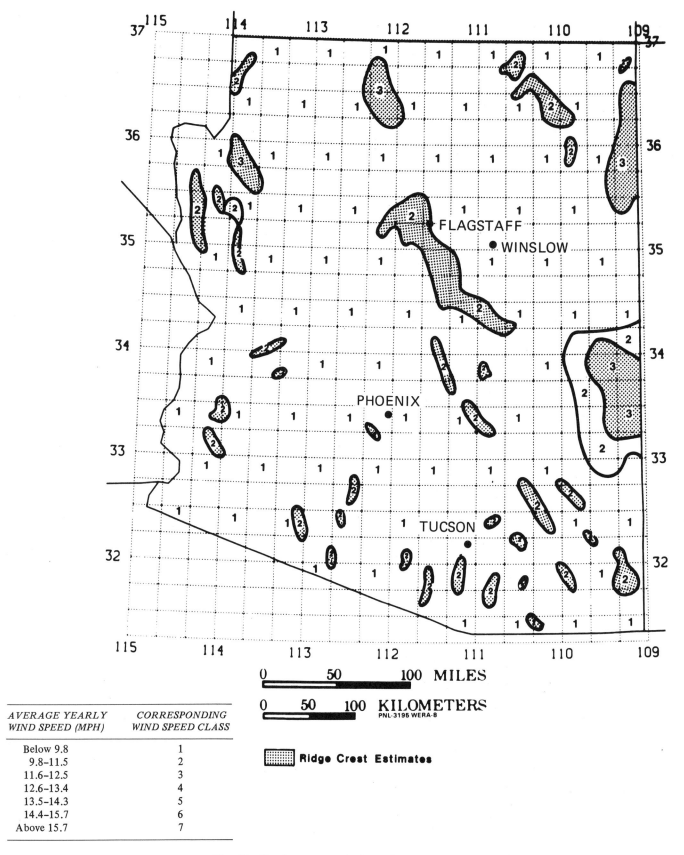

AVERAGE YEARLY WIND SPEED (MPH)	CORRESPONDING WIND SPEED CLASS
Below 9.8	1
9.8–11.5	2
11.6–12.5	3
12.6–13.4	4
13.5–14.3	5
14.4–15.7	6
Above 15.7	7

Ridge Crest Estimates

Fig. 44 Yearly average wind speeds in Arizona.

Monthly average wind speeds at four Arizona locations—Phoenix, Tucson, Winslow, and Flagstaff—are shown in Fig. 47. At Phoenix and Tucson, the seasonal change in wind speed is slight, although the strongest winds occur in spring. Winds are stronger at Tucson than at Phoenix because Phoenix is situated in a basin more than a thousand feet lower. Winds at Tucson are typical of those in the valleys of southern Arizona.

The seasonal patterns at Winslow and Flagstaff are typical of those in the broken terrain of northern Arizona. At both locations, the month of strongest wind is April. The least windy month, however, is August at Flagstaff and January at Winslow. The very light winter winds at Winslow are typical of valley locations in the northern part part of the state. Winter winds are naturally higher on the higher terrain surrounding the valleys.

AVERAGE WIND SPEEDS BY DAY AND NIGHT

In all parts of Arizona, except perhaps on the highest mountains, winds are stronger during the day than at night. Speeds are usually strongest at midafternoon and lightest between midnight and sunrise. The difference between day and night winds is much greater in spring and summer than in autumn and winter.

The day-to-night changes in average wind speed at Phoenix, Tucson, Winslow, and Flagstaff are shown in Fig. 48. Near the southern cities, Phoenix and Tucson, wind speeds average about 3 to 4 mph higher during midafternoon than at dawn, but at Winslow and Flagstaff, in the north, the day–night difference is about 6 mph. In all locations, the difference is greatest on sunny days.

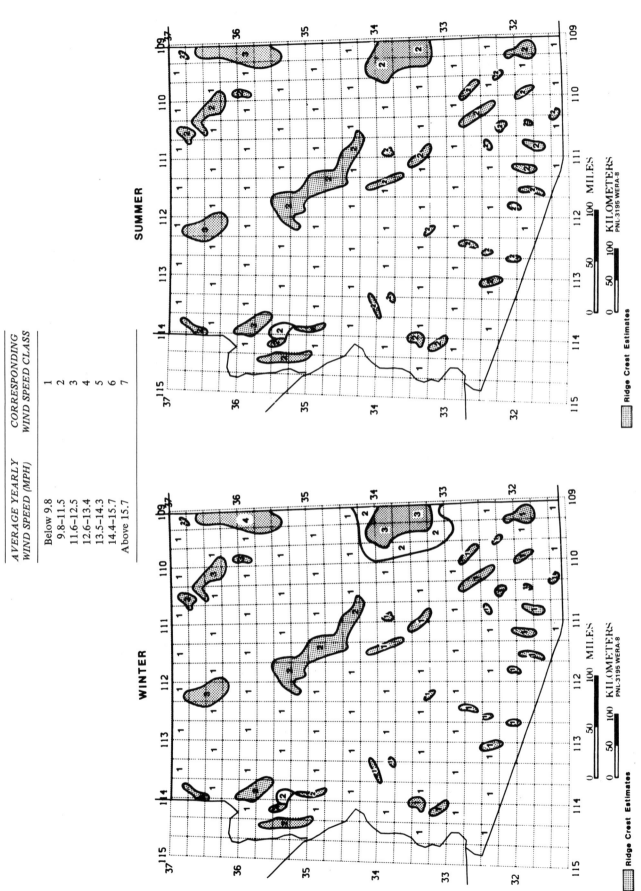

AVERAGE YEARLY WIND SPEED (MPH)	CORRESPONDING WIND SPEED CLASS
Below 9.8	1
9.8–11.5	2
11.6–12.5	3
12.6–13.4	4
13.5–14.3	5
14.4–15.7	6
Above 15.7	7

Fig. 45 Seasonal average wind speeds in Arizona.

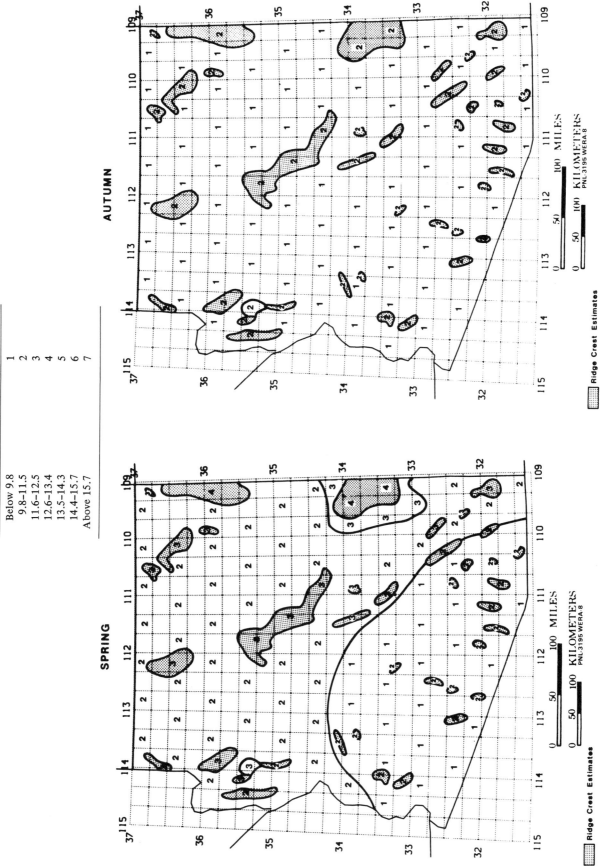

AVERAGE YEARLY WIND SPEED (MPH)	CORRESPONDING WIND SPEED CLASS
Below 9.8	1
9.8–11.5	2
11.6–12.5	3
12.6–13.4	4
13.5–14.3	5
14.4–15.7	6
Above 15.7	7

Fig. 46 Seasonal average wind speeds in Arizona.

ARIZONA

MONTHLY AVERAGE WIND SPEEDS

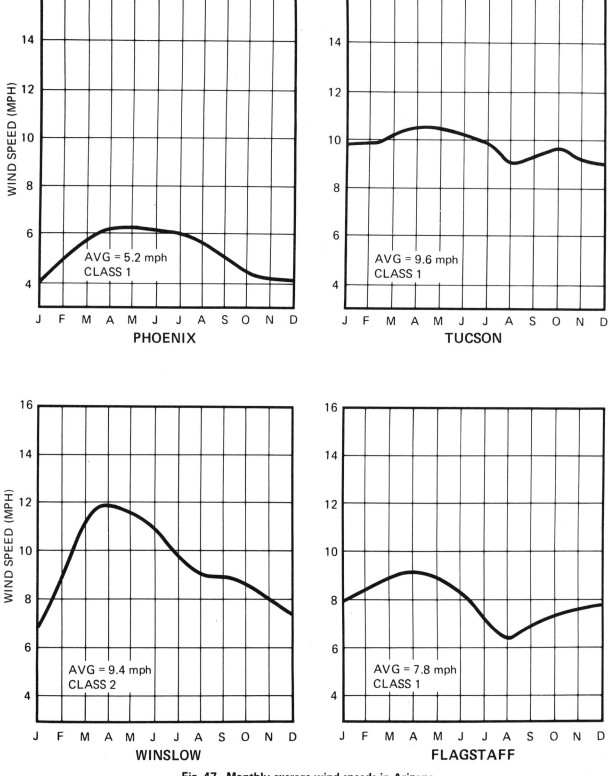

Fig. 47   Monthly average wind speeds in Arizona.

ARIZONA

HOURLY AVERAGE WIND SPEEDS

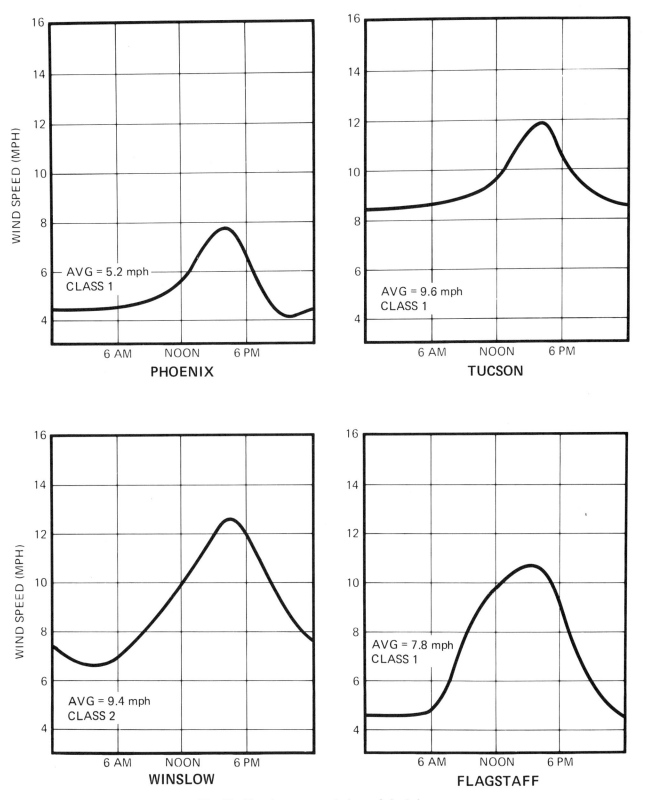

Fig. 48 Hourly average wind speeds in Arizona.

NEW MEXICO

YEARLY AVERAGE WIND SPEEDS

Winds in the northeastern corner of New Mexico as well as many other parts of the state offer at least marginal wind machine sites. However, in Bernalillo County, which includes Albuquerque, and southward through the relatively populous Rio Grande Valley, the winds are not strong enough for wind machines to pay.

Yearly average wind speeds across New Mexico are shown in Fig. 49. Class 4 to Class 5 winds (12.3–14.5 mph) blow over the remote ridges of the highest mountains—the Sacramento, Sangre de Cristo, and San Andres ranges—and over the lower Capulin Mountain in the northeast. Over other mountain summits, the winds are Class 3. More accessible regions of favorable winds can be found over the plains east of the mountain ranges. Speeds there are Class 3 for the most part but reach as high as Class 5 in the extreme northeast, in the vicinity of Clayton. In fact, a site near Clayton was investigated by the Department of Energy for the possible installation of a large federally funded wind machine. Measurements on high terrain about 50 miles west of Clayton indicated the availability of some Class 6 or 7 sites.

Class 3 winds are experienced near Sante Fe as a result of terrain that accelerates the air as it passes between nearby mountain ranges. Other canyons and valleys may have locally stronger winds than those shown in Fig. 49. Winds in the western three-quarters of the state (except for mountain tops) average Class 1 or 2. Most of the Rio Grande Valley and the northwestern quarter of the state experience only Class 1 winds.

SEASONAL AVERAGE WIND SPEEDS

Spring is the windiest season in New Mexico except for its mountain ridges, where winter is windiest. Average wind speeds are shown in Fig. 50 for winter and summer and Fig. 51 for spring and autumn.

During spring, Class 4 winds, or stronger, cover the entire area east of the Rocky Mountains. Class 6 winds, for example, blow over the northeastern corner of the state, and Class 5 winds extend as far as 100 miles west of the Texas border. In the windy section of the Rio Grande Valley near Sante Fe, speeds reach about Class 6. Lighter Class 2 to Class 3 winds blow over the remainder of the lower elevations while on the remote mountain ridges, speeds average Class 4 or 5.

Winds are much lighter over the entire state during summer. In the northeast corner, they drop from Class 6 to Class 3, and in about four-fifths of the state they are only Class 1. On mountain ridges, winds are at their lightest during summer, and autumn brings little improvement. True, winds increase to Class 4 in the northeastern corner and atop the highest mountains, but over most regions they are even lighter in autumn than in summer. During winter, winds are Class 5 in the northeastern corner, Class 2 or Class 3 over the majority

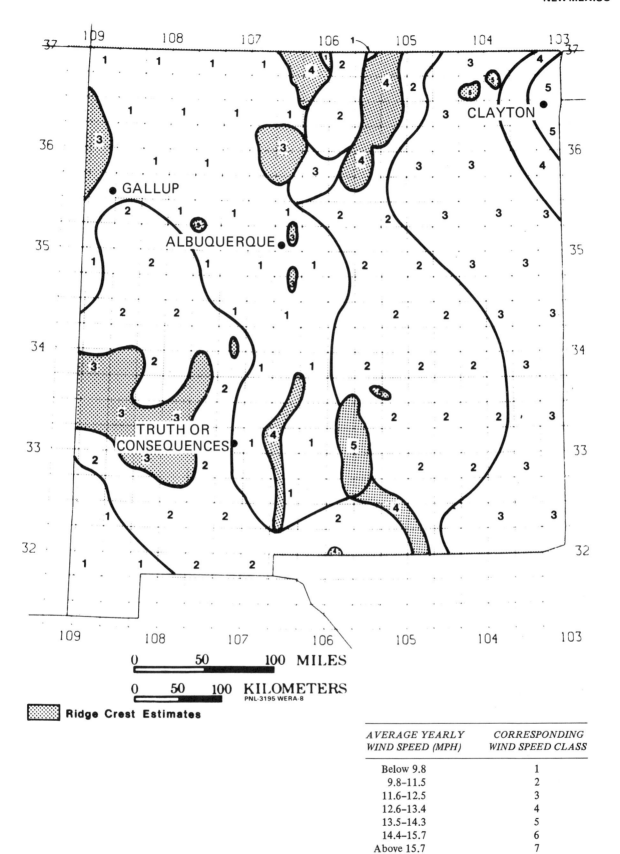

Ridge Crest Estimates

AVERAGE YEARLY WIND SPEED (MPH)	CORRESPONDING WIND SPEED CLASS
Below 9.8	1
9.8–11.5	2
11.6–12.5	3
12.6–13.4	4
13.5–14.3	5
14.4–15.7	6
Above 15.7	7

Fig. 49   Yearly average wind speeds in New Mexico.

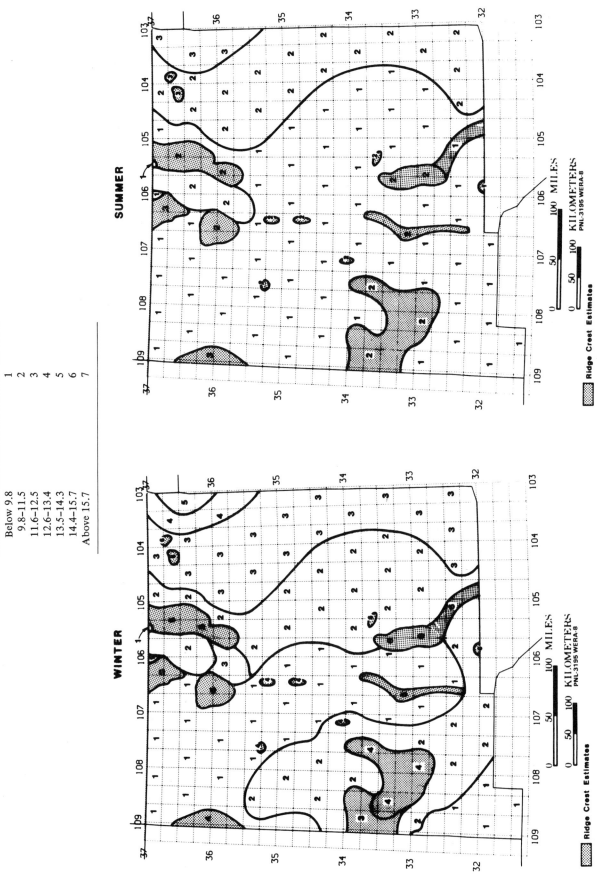

AVERAGE YEARLY WIND SPEED (MPH)	CORRESPONDING WIND SPEED CLASS
Below 9.8	1
9.8–11.5	2
11.6–12.5	3
12.6–13.4	4
13.5–14.3	5
14.4–15.7	6
Above 15.7	7

Fig. 50 Seasonal average wind speeds in New Mexico.

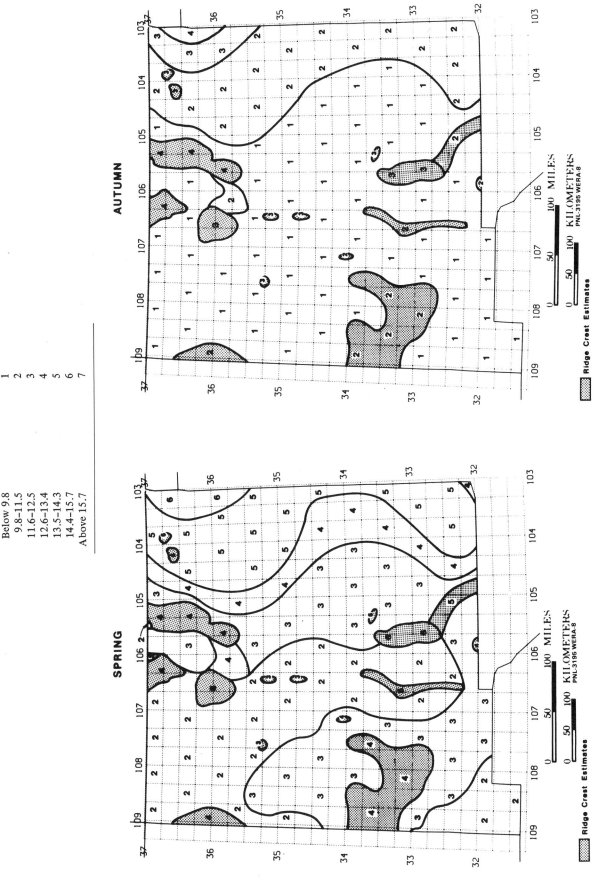

Fig. 51   Seasonal average wind speeds in New Mexico.

of the lower elevations, and as high as Class 6 on mountain ridges, where winter is the windiest season. Winter winds are only Class 1, however, in most of the relatively populous Rio Grande Valley.

Monthly changes in average wind speed at Albuquerque, Gallup, Clayton, and Truth or Consequences are shown in Fig. 52. March or April is the windiest month at each location, and late autumn or winter is the season of lightest wind with the exception of Clayton, where the lightest wind occurs in August. The Clayton pattern is typical of the eastern plains, although winds are lighter over most of them than they are at Clayton. The very light winter winds at Gallup are typical of valley locations in central and western New Mexico. Winter winds are naturally higher on the mesas and plateaus surrounding the valleys.

WIND SPEEDS BY DAY AND NIGHT

Winds are stronger in New Mexico during the day than at night, particularly in the valleys and during spring and early summer. Hourly changes in average wind speed at Albuquerque, Gallup, Clayton, and Truth or Consequences are shown in Fig. 53. At each location, peak wind speeds occur during mid or late afternoon and lowest speeds between midnight and sunrise. At Albuquerque, Clayton, and Truth or Consequences, the average daily difference between the lowest and highest speeds is between 4 and 6 mph. At Gallup, however, which is located in a valley at a high elevation, the cold calm air that normally collects at night results in a day–night difference of nearly 10 mph. This large difference is typical of valley locations.

The increase in wind speed from night to day is much greater in spring and early summer, often twice as great as it is in autumn and early winter. Strong daytime winds are the main reason that spring is New Mexico's windiest season; spring nighttime winds are only slightly stronger, if at all, than those during other seasons.

NEW MEXICO

MONTHLY AVERAGE WIND SPEEDS

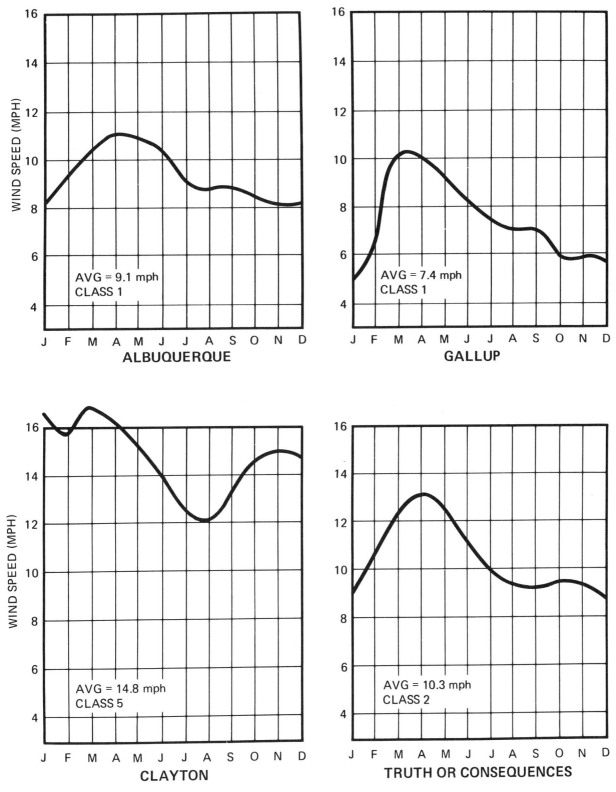

Fig. 52 Monthly average wind speeds in New Mexico.

NEW MEXICO

HOURLY AVERAGE WIND SPEEDS

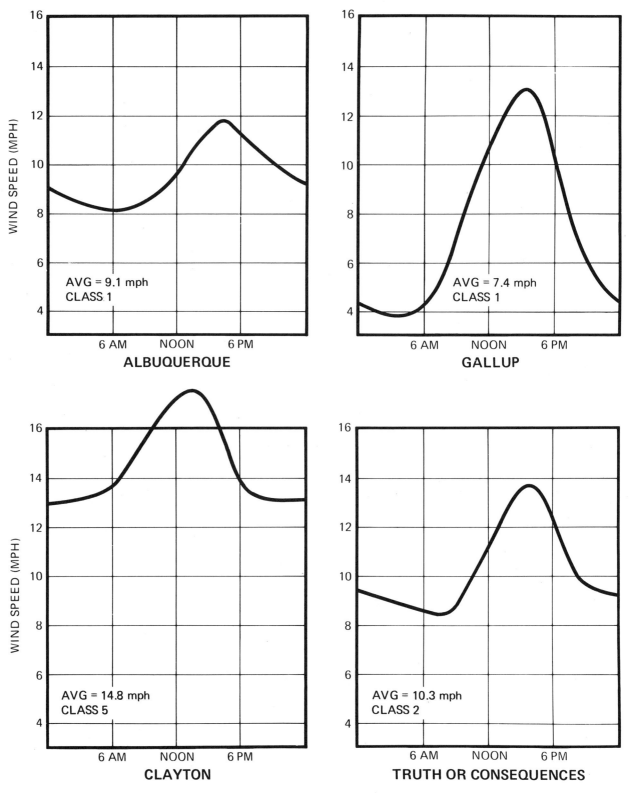

Fig. 53   Hourly average wind speeds in New Mexico.

WIND SPEED AND WIND POWER AT VARIOUS
LOCATIONS IN THE SOUTHWEST

The table that follows shows the yearly average wind speed and the yearly average wind power at each location in the Southwest where winds are measured frequently and reliably. Not enough measurements have been made at other locations to provide the basis for computing reliable yearly averages. (For a definition of wind power and its relationship to average wind speed, refer to page 3.)

TOWN, CITY, OR PLACE	FACILITY	YEARLY AVERAGE WIND SPEED (MPH AT 33 FT ABOVE GROUND)	YEARLY AVERAGE WIND POWER (WATTS PER SQ. METER)
		UTAH	
Bryce Canyon	Bryce Canyon Airport	6.8	53
Cedar City	Cedar City Airport	9.0	100
Delta	Delta Airport	8.5	99
Fairfield	Fairfield Airport	7.6	81
Hanksville	Hanksville Airport	6.0	56
Lucin	Lucin CAA	9.2	90
Milford	Milford Airport	9.0	111
Ogden	Ogden CAA	9.0	79
Ogden	Hill Air Force Base	8.7	89
Salt Lake City	Salt Lake City International Airport	9.4	90
St. George	St. George CAA	6.9	56
Wendover	Wendover Airport	7.4	72
		COLORADO	
Akron	Akron CAA	13.4	234
Alamosa	Alamosa Airport	9.9	131
Aurora	Buckley Field	8.3	65
Colorado Springs	Peterson Field	10.8	112
Denver	Stapleton International Airport	10.1	93
Denver	Aurora Naval Air Station	8.3	58
Eagle	Eagle County Airport	5.4	40
Fort Carson	Butts Air Force Base	10.3	151
Grand Junction	Grand Junction Airport	8.3	62
La Junta	La Junta Airport	8.7	97
Pueblo	Pueblo Memorial Airport	10.1	129
Trinidad	Las Animas County Airport	10.1	122
Air Force Academy	Air Force Academy	9.9	101
		ARIZONA	
Chandler	Williams Air Force Base	5.4	27
Flagstaff	Flagstaff Airport	7.8	52
Fort Huachuca	Libby Air Force Base	6.7	45
Gila Bend	Gila Bend Airport	8.3	57
Payson	Payson Airport	5.6	25
Phoenix	Skyharbor International Airport	5.2	26

TOWN, CITY, OR PLACE	FACILITY	YEARLY AVERAGE WIND SPEED (MPH AT 33 FT ABOVE GROUND)	YEARLY AVERAGE WIND POWER (WATTS PER SQ. METER)
		ARIZONA (continued)	
Phoenix	Litchfield Naval Air Facility	5.2	24
Phoenix	Luke Air Force Base	5.0	27
Prescott	Prescott Airport	9.0	69
Tucson	Tucson International Airport	9.2	87
Tucson	Davis-Monthan Air Force Base	6.3	54
Winslow	Winslow Airport	9.4	111
Yuma	Yuma International Airport	7.8	68
		NEW MEXICO	
Acomita	Acomita Airport	10.3	97
Alamagordo	Holloman Air Force Base	7.2	57
Albuquerque	Albuquerque International Airport	9.2	85
Carlsbad	Carlsbad Airport	11.2	193
Clayton	Clayton Airport	14.8	280
Clovis	Cannon Air Force Base	11.2	130
Clovis	Clovis Airport	11.0	158
Columbus	Hacienda Sur Luna Airport	9.0	101
Farmington	Farmington Airport	8.7	89
Gallup	Gallup Airport	7.4	82
Hobbs	Hobbs Airport	11.9	163
Las Cruces	White Sands Air Force Base	6.9	92
Las Vegas	Las Vegas Airport	11.4	168
Melrose	Melrose Air Force Range	12.1	165
Otto	Otto CAA	7.6	82
Raton	Crews Airport	9.6	151
Roswell	City Weather Bureau Airport Station	10.5	148
Roswell	Walker Air Force Base	9.0	106
Roswell	Roswell Federal Aviation Agency	9.4	91
Santa Fe	Santa Fe Airport	11.9	158
Silver City	Grant County Airport	12.1	150
Truth or Consequences	Truth or Consequences Airport	10.3	129
Tucumcari	Tucumcari Airport	11.9	168
Zuni	Black Rock Airport	9.6	98

5
Southwest Central States

- Kansas
- Oklahoma
- Texas

GENERAL INFORMATION

The Southwest Central Region—especially over the Great Plains of Kansas, Oklahoma, and Texas—has some of the best wind machine sites in the country. The eastern portions of these states, however, especially Texas, have lower wind speeds that are less conducive to the economical production of energy from the wind.

Four areas in particular of the Southwest Central states have appreciable yearly average wind speeds, as shown by the map in Fig. 54. The largest, most important windy area centers on the Texas and Oklahoma Panhandles but extends over much of Kansas, Oklahoma, and northwest Texas. This region is excellent for wind machine energy, not only because of the high average wind speeds but by virtue of the terrain—a mostly flat landscape with sparse vegetation.

Two other regions where winds are as strong as those on the high plains are the crests and summits of the Rocky Mountains in westernmost Texas and the lower, but still rugged, ridges and hilltops of the Ouachita Mountains in eastern Oklahoma. These areas are far smaller, however, as well as less accessible, than the boundless plains.

The fourth region of strong winds is along the coast of the Gulf of Mexico, particularly the shores of lower Texas.

Winds are strongest during spring over most of the Southwest Central states, as shown in Fig. 55. Only the ridge crests of West Texas and a slice of eastern Texas and southeastern Oklahoma experience their strongest winds in winter.

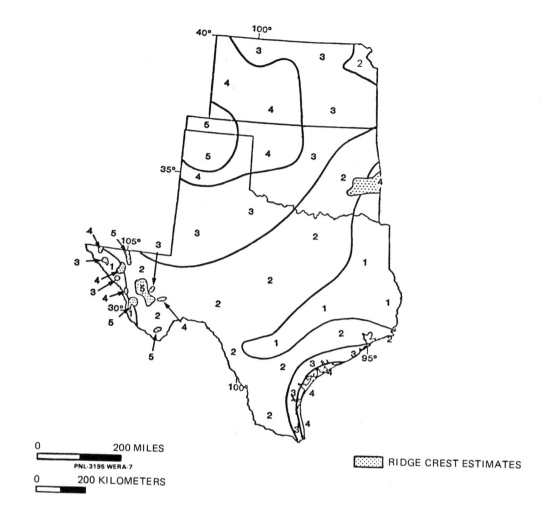

RIDGE CREST ESTIMATES

AVERAGE YEARLY WIND SPEED (MPH)	CORRESPONDING WIND SPEED CLASS
Below 9.8	1
9.8–11.5	2
11.6–12.5	3
12.6–13.4	4
13.5–14.3	5
14.4–15.7	6
Above 15.7	7

Fig. 54 Yearly average wind speeds in the Southwest Central states.

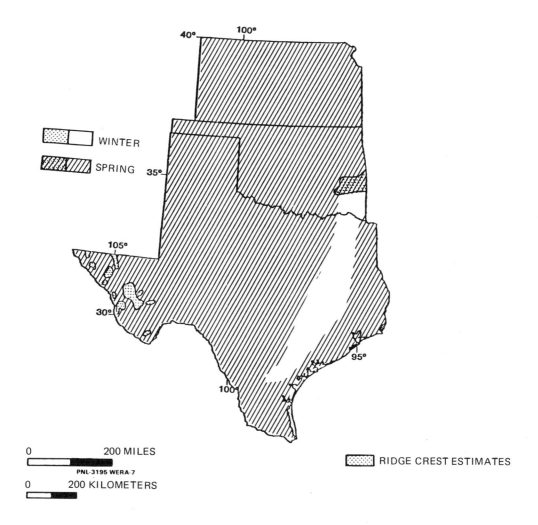

AVERAGE YEARLY WIND SPEED (MPH)	CORRESPONDING WIND SPEED CLASS
Below 9.8	1
9.8–11.5	2
11.6–12.5	3
12.6–13.4	4
13.5–14.3	5
14.4–15.7	6
Above 15.7	7

Fig. 55 Seasons of maximum wind speeds in the Southwest Central states.

KANSAS

YEARLY AVERAGE WIND SPEEDS

Yearly average wind speeds over Kansas average from Class 5 (13.4 to 14.3 mph) in the southwest corner to Class 2 in the northeast corner, as shown in Fig. 56. Rainfall—and hence vegetation—decrease westward over the state, causing higher wind speeds and making it easier to site a wind machine well away from trees. Wind speeds also increase westward with elevation. The only poor wind machine sites in Kansas, in fact, are in the few urban areas and occasional gullies. The flat, dry, and gusty plains of western Kansas still bring back to mind the Dust Bowl days of the 1930s, when a scorching drought turned the soil into a fine dust that these winds drove through screens and cracks into every corner of thousands of hapless farmsteads. The plains were left not only seared but soilless, their inhabitants scattered to less hostile climes.

SEASONAL AVERAGE WIND SPEEDS

Spring is the season of the strongest winds in Kansas, with winter, autumn, and summer following in that order. Figure 57 shows average wind speeds for winter and summer; Fig. 58, those for spring and summer. Speeds reach Class 6 over a large section of western Kansas in spring, and most of the state has at least Class 5 winds; only in the northeastern corner are winds as low as Class 3. Summer, the season of least wind, is marked by Class 1 winds in the eastern part of the state, but even in summer Class 3 winds prevail in the west. Autumn is only slightly windier than summer, but when winter comes, winds again average Class 5 over the southwestern corner and climb to Class 2 in the northeast.

Average wind speeds for each month of the year at four Kansas towns—Topeka, Wichita, Dodge City, and Goodland—are shown in Fig. 59. The spring peak is evident at each location, with either March or April being the windiest month. August is usually the calmest month. At Topeka, winds average 4 mph more in spring than in late summer, whereas at the remaining locations the annual difference is only 3 mph.

AVERAGE WIND SPEEDS BY DAY AND NIGHT

In Kansas, the typical 24-hour wind speed cycle obtains: lowest winds at night, followed by an abrupt increase between dawn and noontime, and strongest winds in the early afternoon, decreasing through late afternoon and evening and leveling out a few hours before midnight. The afternoon peak comes a little later during summer than winter and is most pronounced during late spring.

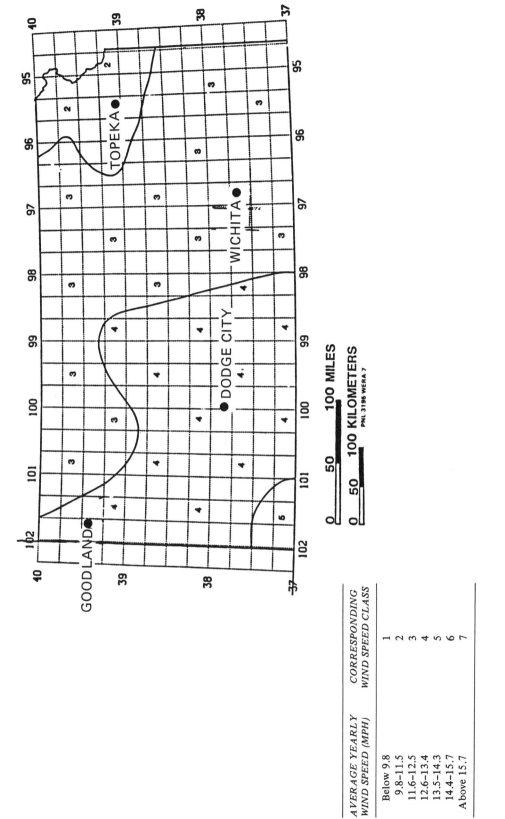

Fig. 56 Yearly average wind speeds in Kansas.

AVERAGE YEARLY WIND SPEED (MPH)	CORRESPONDING WIND SPEED CLASS
Below 9.8	1
9.8–11.5	2
11.6–12.5	3
12.6–13.4	4
13.5–14.3	5
14.4–15.7	6
Above 15.7	7

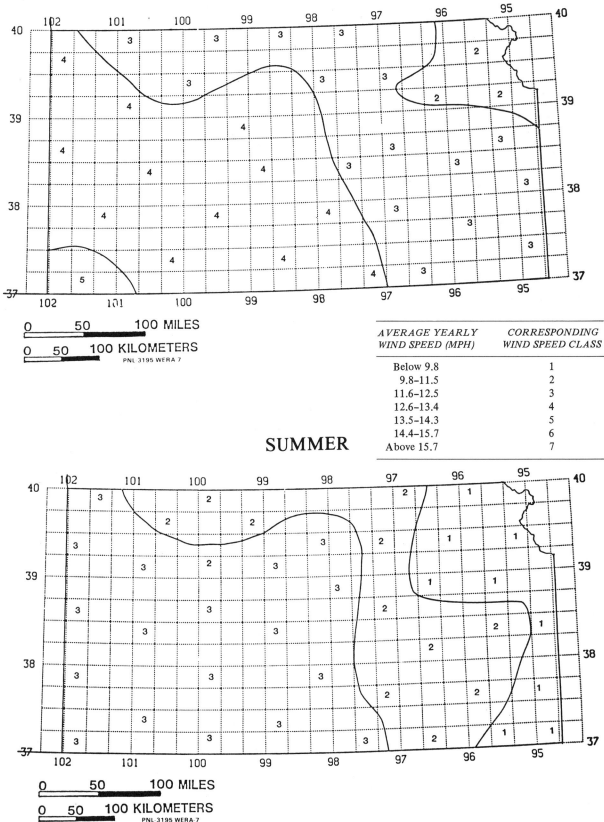

AVERAGE YEARLY WIND SPEED (MPH)	CORRESPONDING WIND SPEED CLASS
Below 9.8	1
9.8–11.5	2
11.6–12.5	3
12.6–13.4	4
13.5–14.3	5
14.4–15.7	6
Above 15.7	7

Fig. 57 Seasonal average wind speeds in Kansas.

SPRING

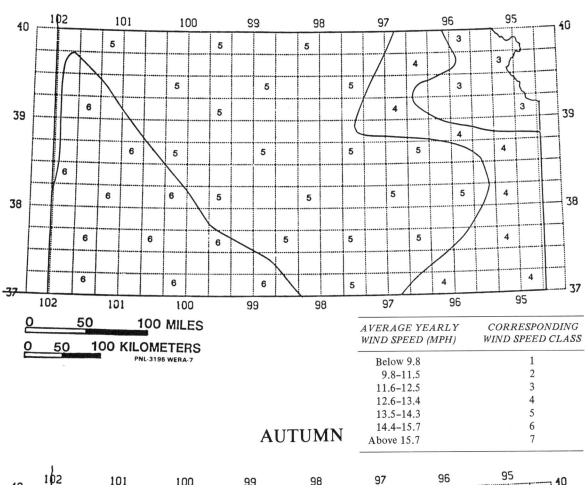

AVERAGE YEARLY WIND SPEED (MPH)	CORRESPONDING WIND SPEED CLASS
Below 9.8	1
9.8–11.5	2
11.6–12.5	3
12.6–13.4	4
13.5–14.3	5
14.4–15.7	6
Above 15.7	7

AUTUMN

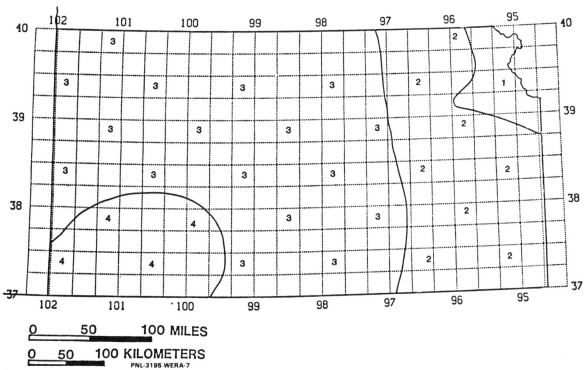

Fig. 58 Seasonal average wind speeds in Kansas.

KANSAS

MONTHLY AVERAGE WIND SPEEDS

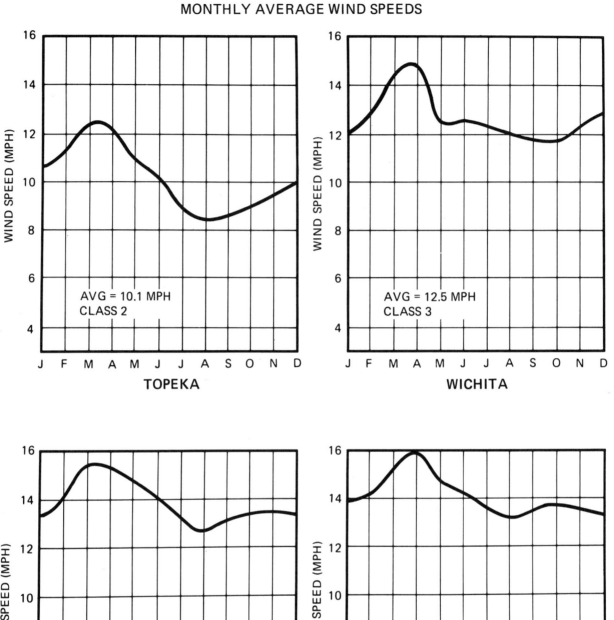

AVG = 10.1 MPH
CLASS 2

TOPEKA

AVG = 12.5 MPH
CLASS 3

WICHITA

AVG = 13.9 MPH
CLASS 4

DODGE CITY

AVG = 13.9 MPH
CLASS 3

GOODLAND

Fig. 59 Monthly average wind speeds in Kansas.

Average wind speeds for the 24-hour daily cycle at Topeka, Wichita, Dodge City, and Goodland are shown in Fig. 60. The greatest day-to-night difference—4 to 5 mph—occurs at the two cities in the east, Topeka and Wichita. In the two western towns, Goodland and Dodge City, winds average only about 3 mph stronger at midday than at night.

KANSAS

HOURLY AVERAGE WIND SPEEDS

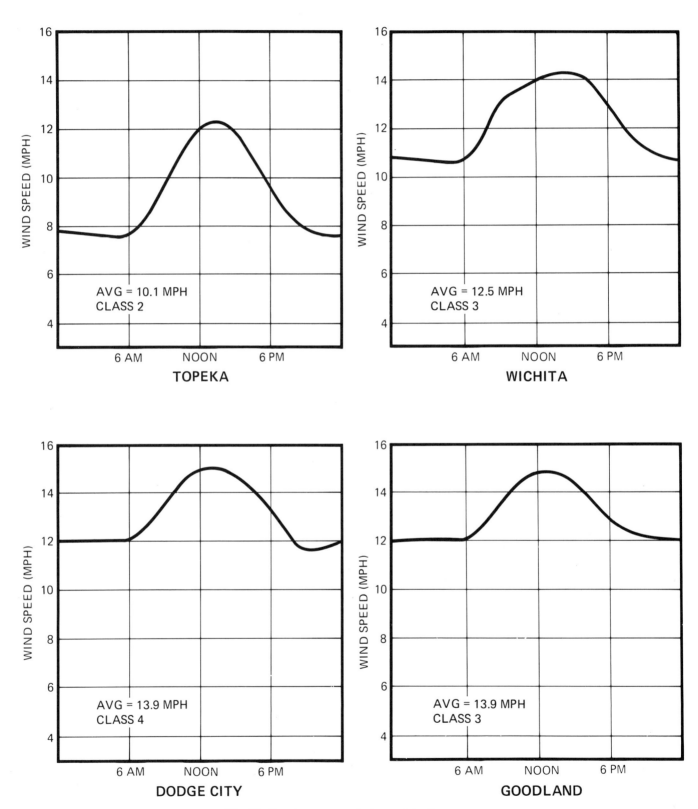

Fig. 60 Hourly average wind speeds in Kansas.

OKLAHOMA

YEARLY AVERAGE WIND SPEEDS

Like Kansas, Oklahoma has strong winds over its western high plains, particularly in the Panhandle, and lighter winds over the eastern part of the state, as shown in Fig. 61. Since most winds come from the south, it is important for wind machine sites to have a clear southern exposure. Winds are especially favorable over higher ground. Speeds are as high as Class 5 (13.4 to 14.3 mph) over the exposed parts of the Panhandle, and favorable Class 4 winds cover a large portion of northwestern Oklahoma. Vegetation is sparse in these Class 4 and 5 areas, making them even more favorable for wind machines; in fact, poor wind machine sites are found only in the few river valleys and urban areas of the state. A strip of central Oklahoma that includes Oklahoma City averages Class 3 winds. This strip is a transitional area between the flat, open, and windy high plains to the west and the more obstructed, forested eastern portion of the state. Average wind speeds drop as low as Class 1 in the southeastern corner, including the lower slopes and many valleys of the Ouachita Mountains (shaded area in Fig. 61). The ridge crests of the Ouachita's, however, are estimated to have Class 4 winds.

SEASONAL AVERAGE WIND SPEEDS

The seasonal changes in Oklahoma winds are shown in Fig. 62, for winter and summer, and in Fig. 63, for autumn and spring. Spring winds are easily the strongest over the entire state except for the few ridge crests of the Ouachita Mountains in the extreme east, where winter winds are stronger (Class 5). Very favorable Class 6 winds blow over much of northwestern Oklahoma during spring, and spring winds are Class 4 or better in about two-thirds of the state. Average wind speeds are about one class lower in winter than in spring, except on those crests of the Ouachita Mountains.

Summer winds are Class 1 throughout the forested eastern portion of the state and Class 3 over the high plains of the northwest. Autumn winds are a bit stronger than summer winds, but the Ouachita Mountain ridge crests are rated only Class 2 during both seasons.

Monthly average wind speeds at Oklahoma City, Tulsa, Gage (in the Panhandle), and Hobart (in the southwest) are shown in Fig. 64. The highest winds occur in March or April at all four locations, and the lowest in late summer. Winds at Oklahoma City and Tulsa vary by nearly 4 mph over the year, but at Gage and Hobart by only 2 mph.

AVERAGE WIND SPEEDS BY DAY AND NIGHT

Winds are stronger during the day than at night in Oklahoma. The lowest speeds come at sunrise and the highest in early afternoon. Winter winds change less between day and night than winds during other seasons; the change is greatest during spring.

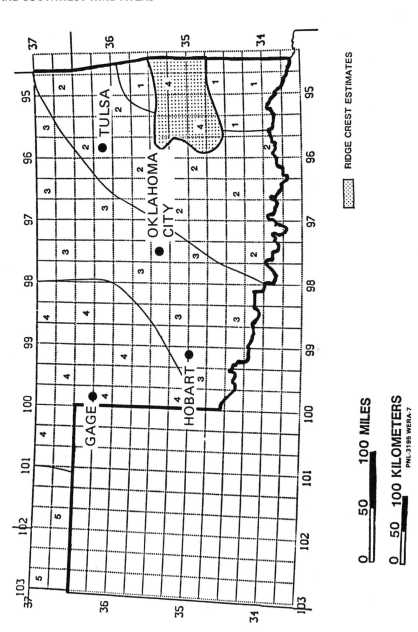

100 MILES

PNL-3195 WERA-7

0   50   100 KILOMETERS

RIDGE CREST ESTIMATES

Fig. 61 Yearly average wind speeds in Oklahoma.

AVERAGE YEARLY WIND SPEED (MPH)	CORRESPONDING WIND SPEED CLASS
Below 9.8	1
9.8–11.5	2
11.6–12.5	3
12.6–13.4	4
13.5–14.3	5
14.4–15.7	6
Above 15.7	7

The hourly variability in wind speed over the 24-hour cycle at the four locations—Oklahoma City, Tulsa, Gage, and Hobart—is shown in Fig. 65. Winds increase very rapidly during the morning and begin to level off before noon at each location. The day-to-night change is greatest at Tulsa (5 mph) and least at Gage (3.5 mph).

WINTER

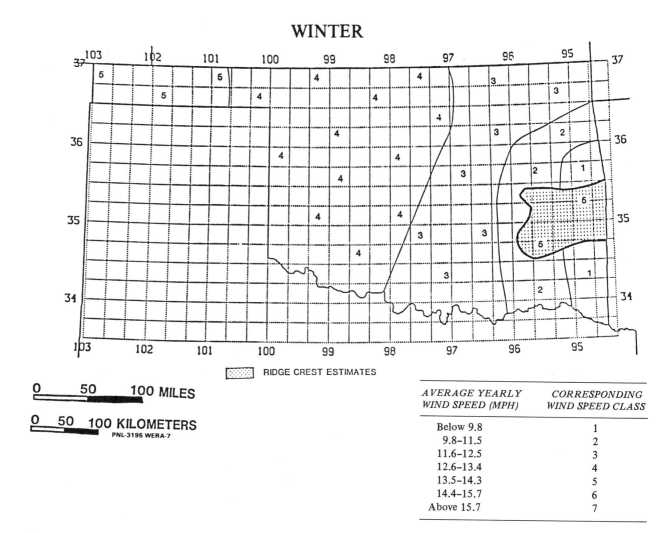

RIDGE CREST ESTIMATES

0 50 100 MILES

0 50 100 KILOMETERS
PNL-3195 WERA-7

AVERAGE YEARLY WIND SPEED (MPH)	CORRESPONDING WIND SPEED CLASS
Below 9.8	1
9.8–11.5	2
11.6–12.5	3
12.6–13.4	4
13.5–14.3	5
14.4–15.7	6
Above 15.7	7

SUMMER

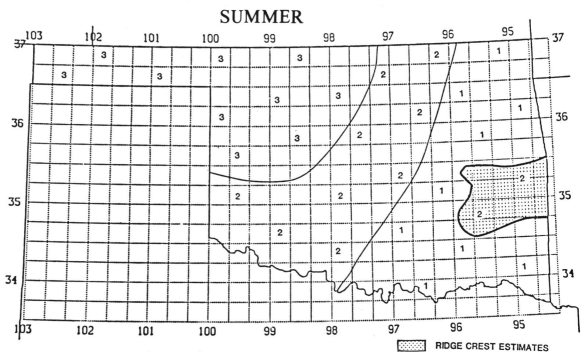

RIDGE CREST ESTIMATES

Fig. 62 Seasonal average wind speeds in Oklahoma.

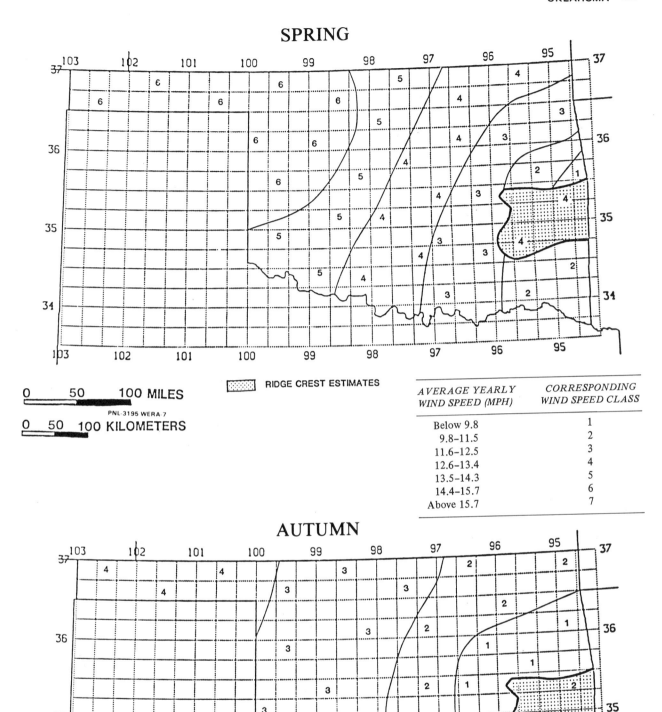

Fig. 63 Seasonal average wind speeds in Oklahoma.

OKLAHOMA

MONTHLY AVERAGE WIND SPEEDS

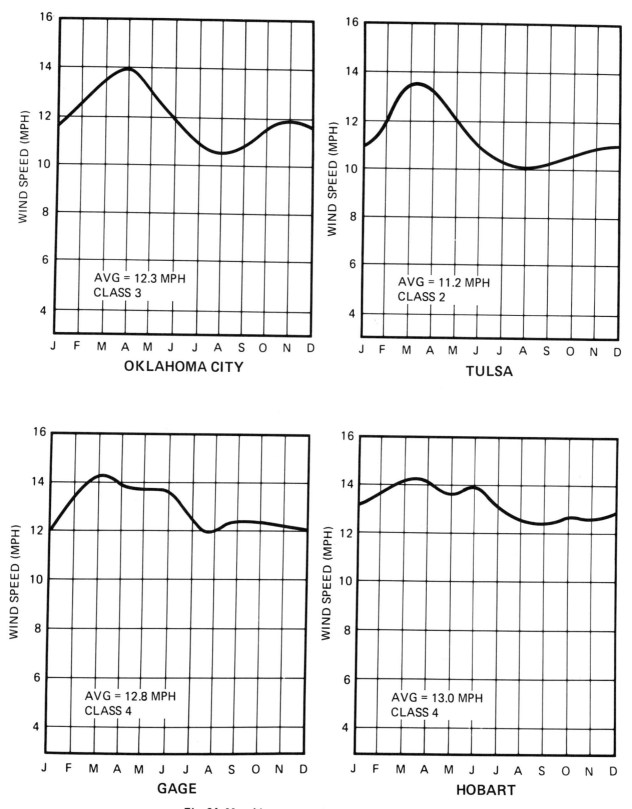

Fig. 64 Monthly average wind speeds in Oklahoma.

OKLAHOMA

HOURLY AVERAGE WIND SPEEDS

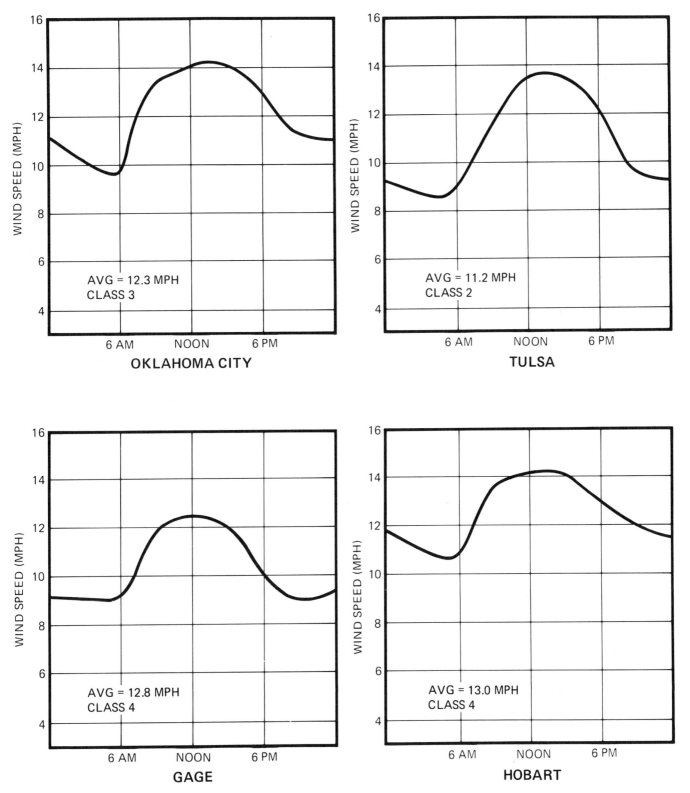

Fig. 65 Hourly average wind speeds in Oklahoma.

WEST TEXAS

YEARLY AVERAGE WIND SPEEDS

Regions of excellent winds for the generation of energy by wind machines exist over much of western Texas, as indicated by Fig. 66. Yearly average wind speeds reach as high as Class 5 (13.4 to 14.3 mph) across the northwestern part of the Panhandle and atop the higher peaks and passes of the Davis and Guadalupe Mountains in far west Texas.

The high plains east of the mountains have yearly average winds of Class 2 to Class 3 northward from the Rio Grande River to where the Panhandle begins. Finding a suitable site for a wind machine on the high plains is comparatively easy because of the lack of vegetation and buildings and the flatness of the terrain. South of the Panhandle, however, the terrain may be frequently broken by hills, mesas, and escarpments. In this region, favorable wind machine sites are limited to whatever crests and summits the landscape affords since winds on the intervening lower ground are predominantly Class 1.

Although the mountainous terrain in extreme west Texas experiences wind speeds of Class 4 to Class 5 over the higher summits and through some of the passes, along the Rio Grande River winds are only Class 1 from El Paso southward to the Big Bend region and Class 2 downriver from there. Large open areas in the west away from the Rio Grande are usually Class 2 as well.

SEASONAL AVERAGE WIND SPEEDS

The seasonal variation in wind speed in west Texas is shown in Fig. 67 for winter and summer and in Fig. 68 for spring and autumn. The strongest winds occur in spring over the entire region except for the crests of the mountains, where they occur in winter.

During spring, winds in the Panhandle average an energetic Class 5 to 6, and only the southernmost part of the region averages as low as Class 2. Winter winds are about one class lower than the winds of spring, except over the peaks and passes in the higher mountains, where Class 7 winds prevail. Autumn winds are about one class lower than those of winter; even over the mountain crests and passes they are only Class 2. The lowest wind speeds occur in summer. Those in the Panhandle are only Class 2 to 3, and south of the Panhandle, including on the highest mountain peaks, they are no higher than Class 1.

Monthly average wind speeds at Amarillo, El Paso, Del Rio, and Guadalupe Pass are shown in Fig. 69. The exceptionally high speeds at Guadalupe Pass peak at 24 mph in January and March, but speeds fall as low as 12 mph in August. At the other three locations, the highest speeds occur in spring or early summer and the lowest in summer or early autumn. The seasonal difference amounts to only 4 mph at these locations, a strong contrast to the 12-mph difference at Guadalupe Pass.

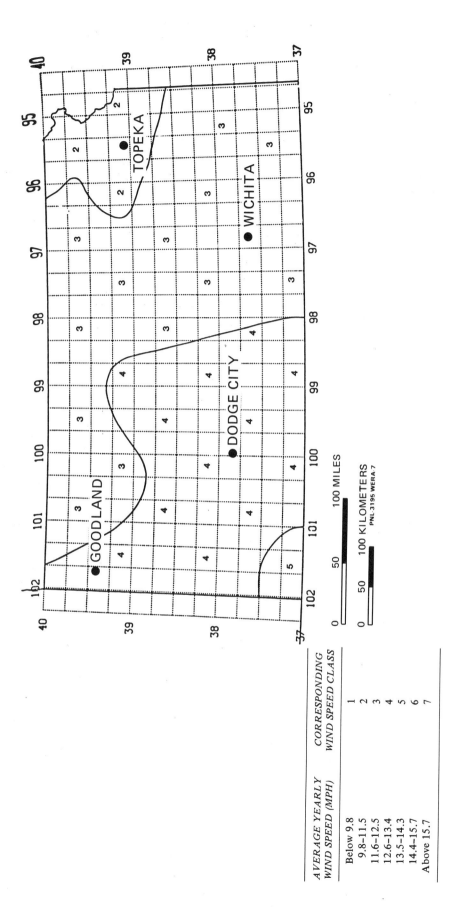

AVERAGE YEARLY WIND SPEED (MPH)	CORRESPONDING WIND SPEED CLASS
Below 9.8	1
9.8–11.5	2
11.6–12.5	3
12.6–13.4	4
13.5–14.3	5
14.4–15.7	6
Above 15.7	7

Fig. 66 Yearly average wind speeds in West Texas.

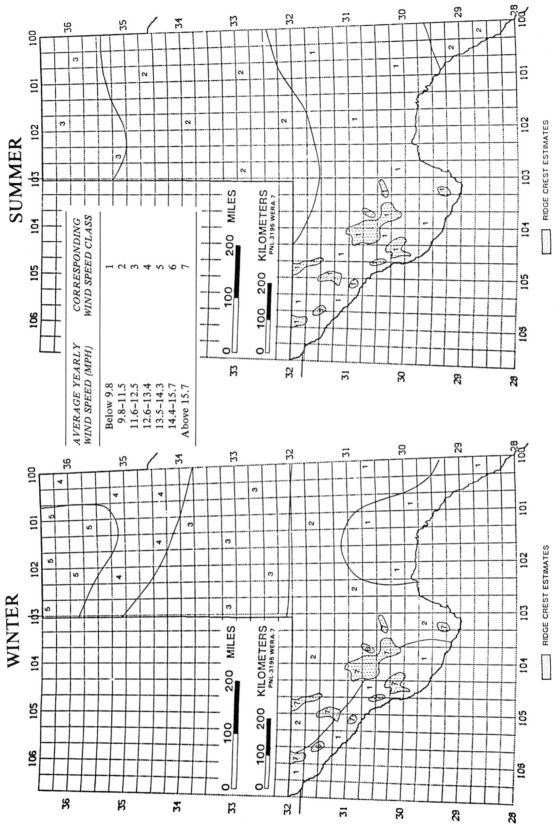

SUMMER

WINTER

AVERAGE YEARLY WIND SPEED (MPH)	CORRESPONDING WIND SPEED CLASS
Below 9.8	1
9.8–11.5	2
11.6–12.5	3
12.6–13.4	4
13.5–14.3	5
14.4–15.7	6
Above 15.7	7

RIDGE CREST ESTIMATES

RIDGE CREST ESTIMATES

Fig. 67 Seasonal average wind speeds in West Texas.

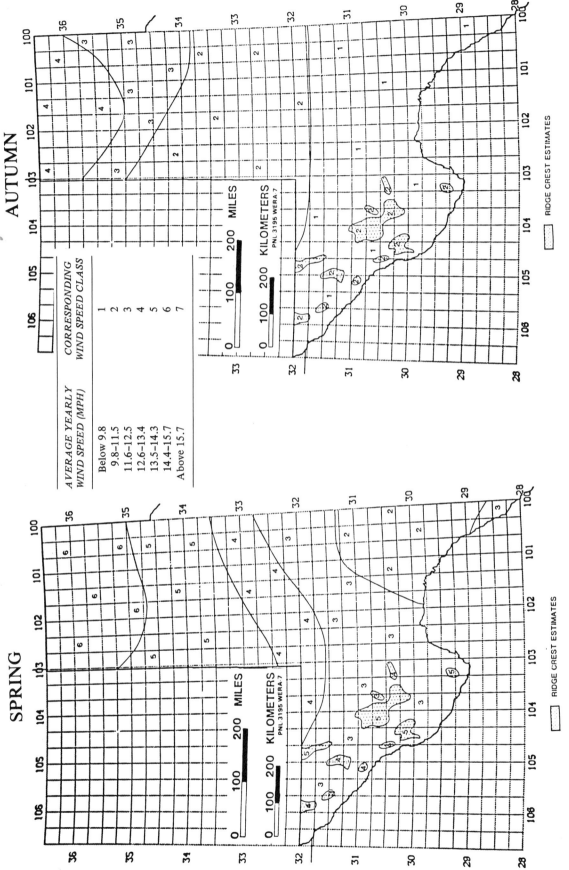

Fig. 68 Seasonal average wind speeds in West Texas.

WEST TEXAS

MONTHLY AVERAGE WIND SPEEDS

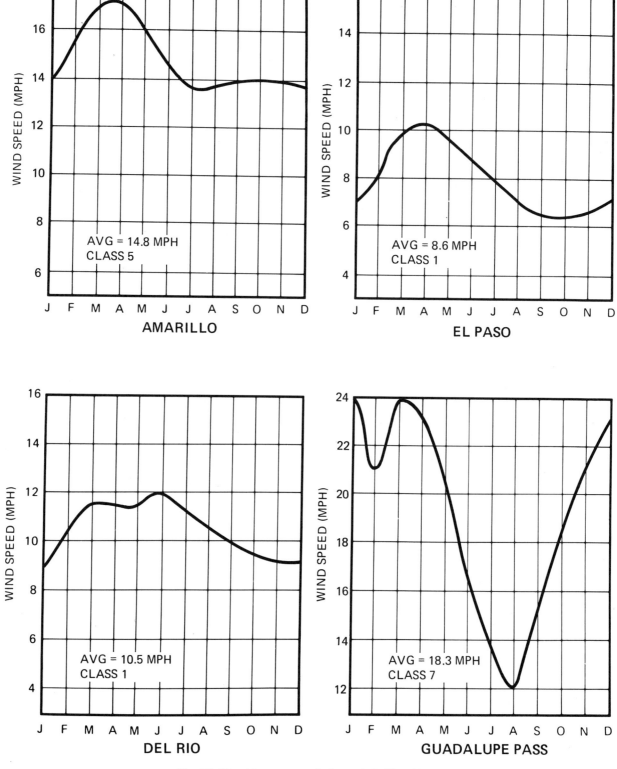

Fig. 69 Monthly average wind speeds in West Texas.

AVERAGE WIND SPEEDS BY DAY AND NIGHT

Wind speeds in West Texas are commonly highest during the afternoon and lowest near sunrise. The 24-hour cycle is shown in Fig. 70 for Amarillo, El Paso, Del Rio, and Guadalupe Pass. The day-night variability is greatest at Guadalupe Pass, where wind speeds average 18 mph at dawn and more than 24 mph in midafternoon. Over mountain peaks winds may vary in a more complex way; highest winds may even occur at night. The difference in wind speeds between day and night amounts to only 2 to 3 mph at the three lower locations. The 24-hour variability is greatest in spring and early summer and least during summer.

WEST TEXAS

HOURLY AVERAGE WIND SPEEDS

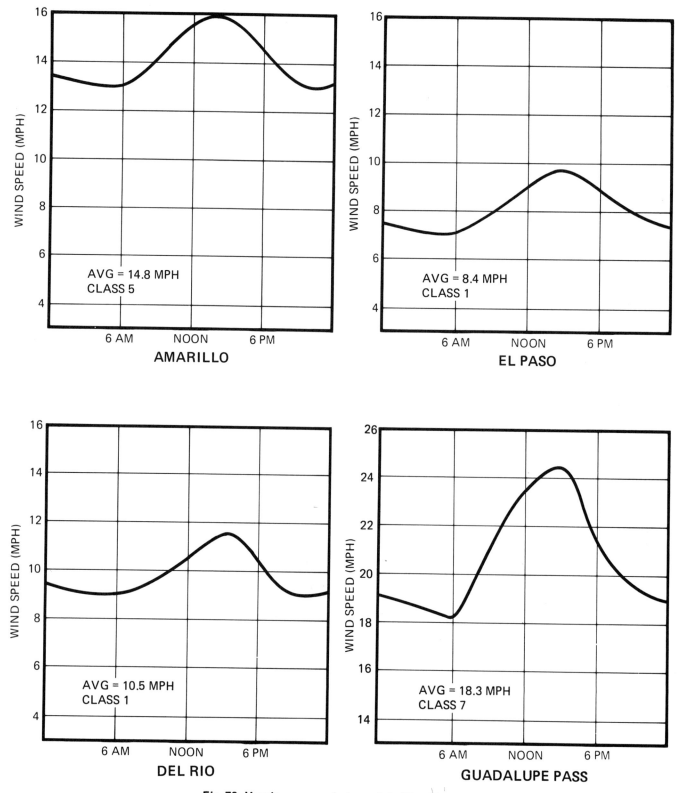

Fig. 70 Hourly average wind speeds in West Texas.

EAST TEXAS

YEARLY AVERAGE WIND SPEEDS

Favorable winds for the production of energy can be found along the coast of the Gulf of Mexico and over the open plains to the west. Forests reduce wind speeds substantially to the east. Yearly average wind speeds are shown in Fig. 71. Prevailing south and southeasterly winds from the Gulf of Mexico whistle unimpeded at a Class-4 clip across San Padre Island and other coastal islands and cities such as Brownsville (slightly inland, near the Mexican border), Corpus Christi, and Galveston. The flatness of the land and lack of vegetation allow these persistent coastal winds to penetrate as much as 50 miles inland at Class 3 speeds. East of Galveston, however, speeds along the coast are reduced to Class 2.

Class 2 winds are the rule over the rest of south Texas and also prevail over the northcentral part of the state, including the Dallas-Ft. Worth area. Farther to the northwest in the direction of the Panhandle, wind speeds rise to Class 3. The eastern part of the state, with a long finger extending far enough west to include San Antonio, experiences only Class 1 winds, largely because of the forests or woods that limit their progress across even large cleared areas.

SEASONAL AVERAGE WIND SPEEDS

Average wind speeds in winter and summer are shown in Fig. 72 and in autumn and spring in Fig. 73. Wind speeds are at their strongest in spring over most of the region; near the Panhandle and along the lower Gulf Coast, they rise as high as Class 5. Winds in winter are nearly as strong—only one class lower than those in spring. In much of the eastern part of the state, speeds remain at Class 1 the year round.

Summer and autumn are the seasons of least wind, Class 1 winds being the rule in most of the region. In the inland part of south Texas, the lightest winds occur in autumn; elsewhere they occur in the summer.

Monthly average wind speeds are shown in Fig. 74 for Houston, Dallas-Ft. Worth, Brownsville, and San Antonio. The windiest months are March or April at each location, and the calmest months are those from late summer to mid-autumn. The difference between the windiest and calmest months is only 2 mph at San Antonio and 4 to 5 mph at the other three locations.

AVERAGE WIND SPEEDS BY DAY AND NIGHT

The difference between daytime and nighttime wind speeds is greater in East Texas than in most regions, particularly just inland from the Gulf of Mexico. The 24-hour cycle of wind speeds is shown in Fig. 75 for Houston, Dallas-Ft. Worth, Brownsville, and San Antonio. At all four locations, the strongest winds blow in the early afternoon and the lightest at sunrise, around 6 A.M. Brownsville winds vary from 7.5 mph near dawn to almost 16 mph in midafternoon. The change is nearly as great at Houston—from 6.5 mph to 13.5 mph. Over the open plains, the day-night difference is only about 4 mph. At all locations, the winds vary more by hour of the day in spring and summer than they do during autumn and winter.

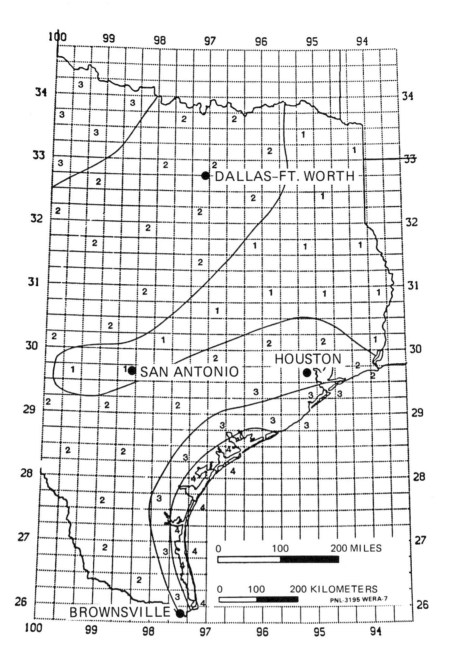

AVERAGE YEARLY WIND SPEED (MPH)	CORRESPONDING WIND SPEED CLASS
Below 9.8	1
9.8–11.5	2
11.6–12.5	3
12.6–13.4	4
13.5–14.3	5
14.4–15.7	6
Above 15.7	7

Fig. 71 Yearly average wind speeds in East Texas.

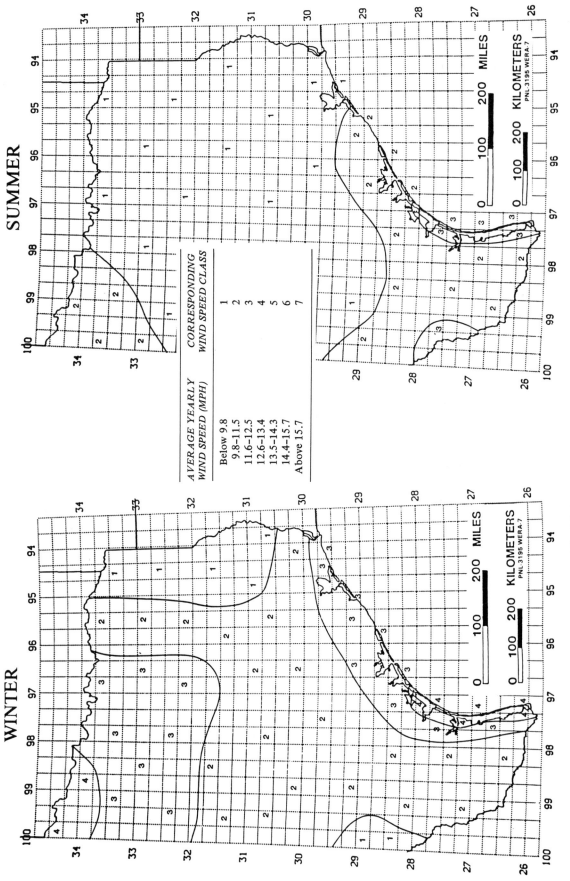

AVERAGE YEARLY WIND SPEED (MPH)	CORRESPONDING WIND SPEED CLASS
Below 9.8	1
9.8–11.5	2
11.6–12.5	3
12.6–13.4	4
13.5–14.3	5
14.4–15.7	6
Above 15.7	7

Fig. 72 Seasonal average wind speeds in East Texas.

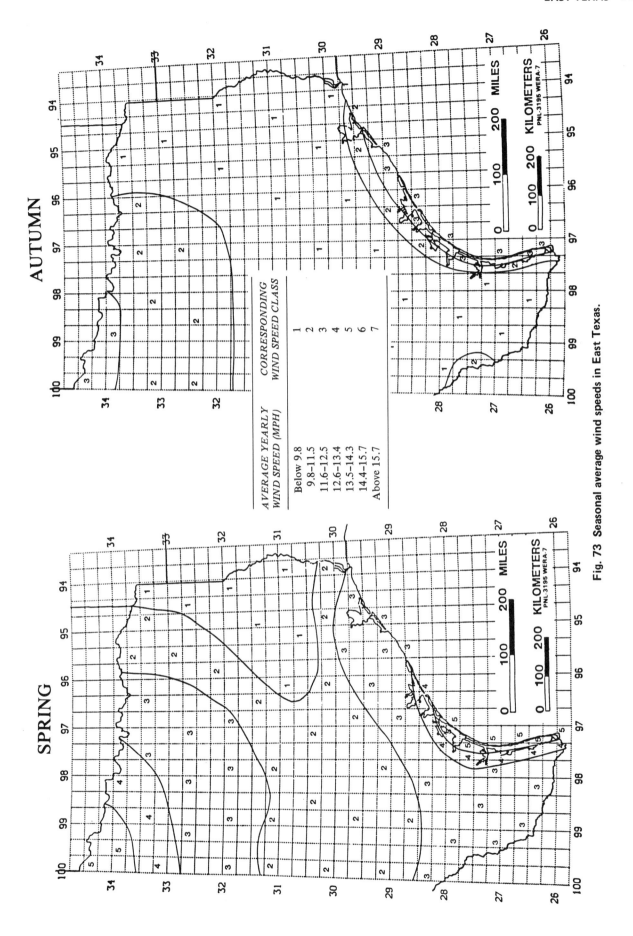

AUTUMN

SPRING

AVERAGE YEARLY WIND SPEED (MPH)	CORRESPONDING WIND SPEED CLASS
Below 9.8	1
9.8–11.5	2
11.6–12.5	3
12.6–13.4	4
13.5–14.3	5
14.4–15.7	6
Above 15.7	7

Fig. 73 Seasonal average wind speeds in East Texas.

EAST TEXAS

MONTHLY AVERAGE WIND SPEEDS

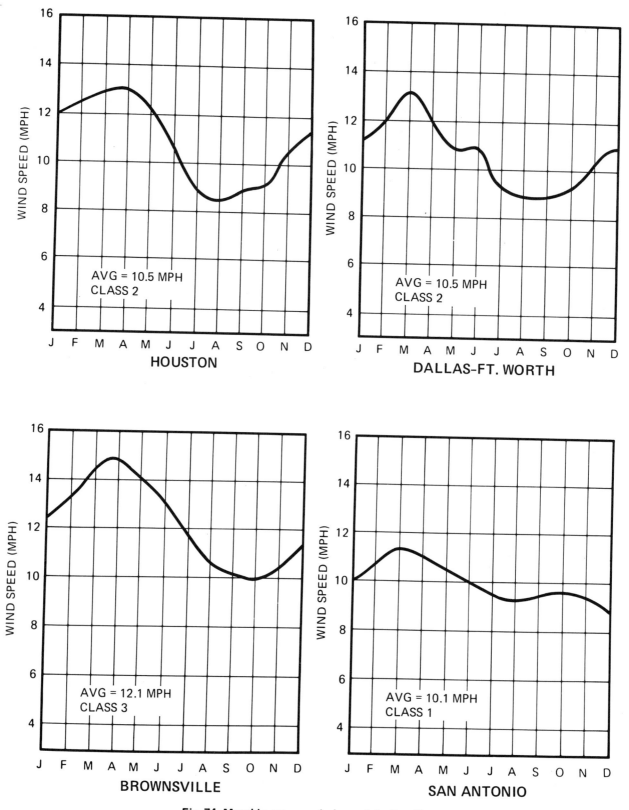

Fig. 74 Monthly average wind speeds in East Texas.

EAST TEXAS

HOURLY AVERAGE WIND SPEEDS

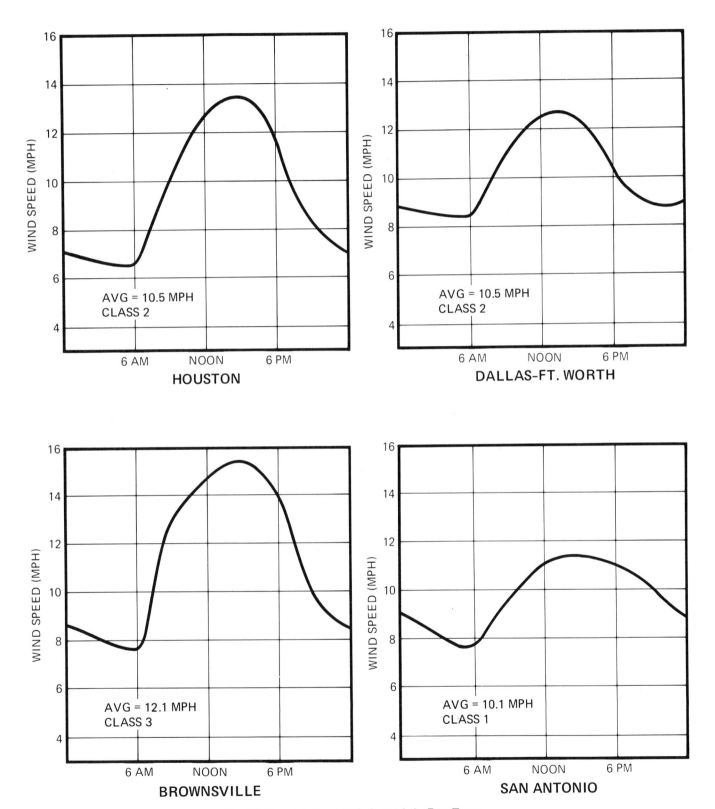

Fig. 75 Hourly average wind speeds in East Texas.

WIND SPEED AND WIND POWER AT VARIOUS LOCATIONS IN THE SOUTHWEST CENTRAL STATES

The table that follows shows the yearly average wind speed and the yearly average wind power at each location in Kansas, Oklahoma, and Texas where winds are measured frequently and reliably. Not enough measurements have been made at other locations to provide the basis for computing reliable yearly averages. (For a definition of wind power and its relationship to average wind speed, refer to page 3.)

TOWN, CITY OR PLACE	FACILITY	YEARLY AVERAGE WIND SPEED (MPH AT 33 FT ABOVE GROUND)	YEARLY AVERAGE WIND POWER (WATTS PER SQ. METER)
KANSAS			
Anthony	Anthony Civil Aeronautics Adm.	11.6	180
Chanute	Martin Johnson Airport	12.3	164
Concordia	Riosser Airport	13.0	193
Dodge City	Municipal Airport	13.9	226
Emporia	Emporia Airport	12.3	193
Ft. Leavenworth	Sherman Army Air Field	6.9	62
Ft. Riley	Marshall Army Air Field	8.7	122
Garden City	Garden City Civil Aeronautics Adm.	11.9	224
Goodland	Renner Field Airport	13.8	218
Hill City	Hill City Municipal Airport	11.2	176
Hutchinson	Hutchinson Naval Air Station	12.8	210
Lebo	Lebo Civil Aeronautics Adm.	11.4	170
Olathe	Olathe Naval Air Station	9.9	117
Russell	Russell Municipal Airport	13.7	210
Salina	Salina Airport	12.6	219
Salina	Salina Air Force Base	10.8	166
Topeka	Billard Airport	10.1	117
Wichita	Wichita Municipal Airport	12.5	190
OKLAHOMA			
Altus	Altus Air Force Base	10.5	159
Ardmore	Ardmore Civil Aeronautics Adm.	9.9	118
Clinton	Clinton-Sherman Air Force Base	13.0	235
Enid	Enid Airport	12.5	226
Ft. Sill	Ft. Sill Army Signal Corp.	9.6	134
Gage	Gage Airport	12.8	216
Gene Autrey	Ardmore Air Force Base	7.4	73
Hobart	Hobart Airport	13.0	215
Oklahoma City	Oklahoma City Airport	13.4	244
Ponca City	Ponca City Airport	12.8	190
Tulsa	Tulsa Airport	11.0	141

TOWN, CITY, OR PLACE	FACILITY	YEARLY AVERAGE WIND SPEED (MPH AT 33 FT ABOVE GROUND)	YEARLY AVERAGE WIND POWER (WATTS PER SQ. METER)
		WEST TEXAS	
Amarillo	English Field Airport	14.8	252
Big Spring	Big Spring Supplementary Aviation Weather Reporting	11.6	162
Childress	Childress Airport	11.6	159
Clarendon	Clarendon Airport	12.5	186
Dalhart	Dalhart Airport	13.7	251
Del Rio	International Airport	10.5	99
El Paso	Biggs Air Force Base	7.6	86
Guadalupe Pass	Guadalupe Pass Civil Aeronautics Adm.	18.4	695
Lubbock	West Texas Air Terminal	12.1	162
Marfa	Marfa Airport	10.3	132
Midland	Mid-Odessa Regional Air Terminal	12.3	158
Salt Flat	Salt Flat Civil Aeronautics Adm.	8.1	98
San Angelo	Mathis Field Airport	10.8	119
Wink	Winkler County Airport	9.6	111
		EAST TEXAS	
Abilene	Municipal Airport	12.3	166
Abilene/Dyess	Dyess Air Force Base	9.9	119
Alice	Alice Airport	11.2	159
Austin	Mueller Airport	9.9	99
Beesville	Chase Field Naval Auxiliary Air Station	8.7	94
Brownsville	Rio Grande International Airport	12.1	178
Bryan	Bryan Air Force Base	7.6	64
Corpus Christi	Corpus Christi Naval Air Station	12.8	200
Corpus Christi	Corpus Christi Airport	12.8	194
Cotulla	Cotulla Municipal Airport	9.6	102
Dallas	Dallas Naval Air Station	9.0	90
Dallas	Love Field Weather Bureau Airport Stn.	12.1	152
Ft. Hood	Gray Air Force Base	11.2	146
Ft. Worth	Carswell Air Force Base	9.6	125
Ft. Worth	Greater Southwest International Airport	10.5	121
Galveston	Scholes Field Airport	12.1	165
Harlingen	Harlingen Air Force Base	9.6	118
Houston	Houston International Airport	8.1	62
Houston	Hobby Airport	10.5	126
Junction	Junction Airport	7.2	51
Kingsville	Kingsville Naval Auxiliary Air Station	9.2	104
Laredo	Laredo Municipal Airport	11.6	152
Longview	Longview Airport	9.6	85
Lufkin	Angelina County Airport	7.8	56
Matagorda Is.	Matagorda Airfield	12.3	178
Mineral Wells	Mineral Wells Municipal Airport	10.8	127
Palacios	Palacios Airport	11.0	123
Port Arthur	Jefferson County Airport	10.3	111

TOWN, CITY, OR PLACE	FACILITY	YEARLY AVERAGE WIND SPEED (MPH AT 33 FT ABOVE GROUND)	YEARLY AVERAGE WIND POWER (WATTS PER SQ. METER)
	EAST TEXAS (continued)		
Port Isabel	Port Isabel Naval Auxiliary Air Station	13.9	254
San Antonio	San Antonio International Airport	10.1	79
Sherman	Perrin Air Force Base	10.5	137
Tyler	Tyler Airport	9.6	103
Victoria	Victoria Airport	10.8	126
Waco	James Connally Air Force Base	9.0	100
Waco	Waco Municipal Airport	11.2	139
Wichita Falls	Wichita Falls Airport	12.5	191